THE CLASH

Clas

trosp Ctive

RETRO PUBLISHING

2S0773

Published by:

RETRO PUBLISHING
P.O. Box 5
16 Notting Hill Gate
London W11 3JE

CONTENTS

Introduction	5
A Brief History	7
White Riot	19
Capital Radio	21
Remote Control	22
Complete Control	23
Clash City Rockers	24
White Man in Hammersmith Palais	25
Tommy Gun	26
English Civil War	27
Cost of Living EP	28
I fought the Law	29
London Calling	30
Train in Vain (Stand By Me)	33
Rudie Can't Fail	36
Clampdown	37
Somebody got Murdered	37
The Clash Singles ... Japanese Box Set	38
Bankrobber	40
The Call Up	41
Hitsville UK	42
The Magnificent Seven	43
This is Radio Clash	46
Know your Rights	48
Rock the Casbah	50
Should I Stay or Should I Go / Straight to Hell	53
This is England	57
Return to Brixton	59
Collaborations: Janie Jones & The Lash; Futura 2000; Tymon Dogg	60

CONTENTS

The Clash	61
Give 'em Enough Rope	65
London Calling	69
Black Market Clash	73
Sandinista!	74
If Music could Talk	79
Spirit of St Louis (Ellen Foley)	80
Combat Rock ... Rat Patrol from Fort Bragg	81
The World according to the Clash	85
Super Black Market Clash	86
Cut the Crap	87
The Story of the Clash Volume 1	90
Crucial Music	92
The Singles	93
Twelve Inch Mixes	94
Clash on Broadway	95
The Clash Bootleg Bible	97
The Clash UK Gig Guide ... Confirmed Sightings	112

Introduction

The Clash `Westway Rockers' Lieutenants to the Punk explosion.   When The Sex Pistols kicked down the doors, The Clash led the charge, broke punk mainstream and took America by storm. `The Last Gang in Town', this is their story.

In over ten years together they covered many musical styles on their double/triple album releases - Rockabilly, Hip Hop, Raga, Reggae, Rock'n'Roll, and last but not least, good old Punk Rock. But would we really have wanted to hear the first album sound over the next five album releases, fab that it was!? ... I think not ... to big `sold out' cry the crowd. Would we really have liked the lads more if they sold no records and failed ... I think not also.

The Clash, the political arm to The Sex Pistols' boot - whether or not you believe `Punk died the day The Clash signed to CBS' depends on what fence you have built for yourself. But the world would be a lesser place if we were denied some Clash tracks blasting from the hi-fi ...

Elvis, The Beatles and The Rolling Stones did not go away after all, and neither should The Clash, sit back and enjoy what the chaps got up to. As the saying goes, `There's something here for everyone' - classic singles, classic pop, political songs and some humour too ... fill in what goes where yourself.

For further reading, check out Marcus Gray's tombstone `Last Gang in Town', but please keep a copy of this book by your side at all times - questions will be asked come the revolution.

Putting on the editors hat for a moment just to say 'For those on the cutting room floor (Foreign 7"singles no picture sleeves etc,,etc ,)...   We Salute you...

Thanx to Faith for patience FAITH xx   PETE & Keith without whom....
Rocking Robin & Marco Matrix for fine tuning & God The Clash....

Flick through these pages carefully ... a history lesson for one and all ... what more to say except:

"If you don't like The Clash ... you don't like Rock'n'Roll"

Enjoy,

Your friendly
Agent Provocateur

SLOGANS

hate & war

Sten guns in Knightsbridge

heavy duty Discipline

Rebel Bluce

an Advance is a loan

Knives in W11

Creative violence

heavy Manners

white Riot

Compliance to defiance two steps away

Brigade Rosse

Janie Jones

A Brief History

1973-1974

Woody Mellor (born John Mellor 21/ 8/ 1952 Ankara, Turkey) plays gigs in his first band in Newport, South Wales. Originally called `Flaming Youth', but Woody (in recognition of Woody Guturie, the American singer/songwriter) renames them `The Vultures'.

1974

Mick Jones (born 26/ 6/ 1955 Brixton, London) plays in various `Mott the Hoople' influenced bands `The Delinquents', `Little Queenie'.

19 June 1974

Mick Jones plays first ever gig with `The Delinquents' at Queen Elizabeth College, Kensington, London.

1974

Mick Jones has ill-fated rehearsals with Chrissie Hynde (later of The Pretenders) to form a group `Big Girls Underwear'.

1974

Woody Heads to London, moves into a squat at 101 Walterton Road and jams with its occupants; the `101 Allstars' are formed, soon to be shortened to the `101'ers'.

March 1975

Mick Jones forms `London SS' with Tony James (Generation X), a group that at one time or another consisted of various members of `The Damned', `Pretenders', `Subterraneans' and `The Boys'. This seminal non-gigging punk outfit ... waiting for a scene to happen ...

November 1975

A chance meeting with Mick Jones through a friend sees Paul Simonon (born 6/8/1955) auditioning for vocalists job in `London SS'.

1975

Woody changes his name to Joe (as in any old Joe) Strummer (to suit his limited guitar style, just strumming).

1975-mid 1976

101'ers tour pub circuit and release single `Keys to your Heart'/`5 Star Rock'n'Roll Petrol' on Chiswick Records.

January 1976

`London SS' dissolves due to people leaving to form other bands. Mick is encouraged by Bernie Rhodes (Malcolm McClarens' co-conspirator) to form a new band which he will manage.

March 1976

Mick, while attending Hammersmith School of Art (Lime Grove, Shepherds Bush) meets up with Paul Simonon again and his accomplices in a squat in Davis Road, Shepherds Bush. They form a band, `The Heartdrops'. Mick Jones (guitar, vocals), Keith Levene (Guitar), Paul Simonon (bass).

A Brief History

3 April 1976

101'ers play The Nashville Rooms, Kensington, supported by `The Sex Pistols'. After the gig, Mick Jones and Paul Simonon tell Joe Strummer that he was great but his band were `shit'. Joe's memories of that gig were, `As soon as I saw them (Sex Pistols), I just knew'.

30 May 1976

Bernie Rhodes, on seeing the 101'ers at the Golden Lion, Fulham, tells Joe he is putting a band together to rival The Sex Pistols. He is given 48 hours to make up his mind, he takes 24 ... the group is formed: Joe Strummer (guitar/vocals), Mick Jones (guitar/vocals), Keith Levene (guitar), Paul Simonon (bass).

June 1976

Bernie Rhodes moves `The Clash' to a rehearsal place next door to the Roundhouse venue in Camden Town. They christen it `Rehearsal Rehearsal'.

June 1976

Pablo Labritain (later to form `999'), a friend of Joe's, sits in on drums on first few rehearsals, but on calling back Terry Chimes who had auditioned for `London SS', the Clash now have a drummer.

June 1976

After various name changes - `Phones', `Mirrors', `Psycho Negatives', `Heartdrops' - all lasting about a week, Paul Simonon, on looking through The Evening Standard newspaper, notices the word `Clash' reappearing. Clash as in culture, violence, etc. It's put to the vote ... it's in ... the band now have a name, `The Clash'.

June/July 1976

Sebastian Conran (son of Terence Conran, furniture design, etc.) befriends the group and becomes Bernie Rhode's assistant, helping out by designing their `Jackson Pollock' look clothes/image and early poster/flyer designs.

4 July 1976

The Clash play their first gig supporting The Sex Pistols at the Black Swan in Sheffield.

13 August 1976

Second show, a private performance for friends and press at their rehearsal studios in Camden Town. Here they preview their splattered paint and slogans image for the first time.

29 August 1976

The Clash play with The Sex Pistols at the Screen on the Green, Islington - the Midnight Special Show, their first public gig in London.

31 August 1976

The Clash play the 100 Club, London, supporting The Sex Pistols.

5 September 1976

The Clash play The Roundhouse, Camden Town, supporting The Kursal Flyers. This history tells us it will be Keith Levene's fifth and last gig with The Clash (he will go on to form P.I.L. with John Lydon). On his leaving, Joe Strummer quotes, "He had some urgent business in North London"

A Brief History

20 September 1976

The Clash play the first night of the Punk Festival at the 100 Club, second on the bill to The Sex Pistols, along with Vic Godard and Subway Sect (also managed by Bernie Rhodes) and Suzi and the Banshees (their first gig with Sid Vicious on drums).

9 October 1976

The Clash play Tiddenfoot Leisure Centre in Leyton Buzzard supporting The Rockets.

15 October 1976

The Clash play Acklam Hall, Ladbroke Grove, London.

16 October 1976

Play University of London, third on the bill to Shaking Stevens.

23 October 1976

Play `A Night of Pure Energy' at the ICA (Institute of Contemporary Arts) supported by Subway Sect. In the crowd that night is one Steve Connally, just out of prison. Needing somewhere to stay and being impressed with The Clash, he becomes their roadie and is rechristened `Rodent'.

27 October 1976

Play Barbarellas Birmingham, supporting Surburban Studs.

29 October 1976

Play Fulham Town Hall, London, supporting Roogalator.

5 November 1976

Play `A Night of Treason' at RCA (The Royal College of Art), supported by The Rockets and Subway Sect.

11 November 1976

Play The Lacy Lady, Ilford, supported by Subway Sect.

Mid November 1976

A&R man, Chris Perry (who just missed signing The Sex Pistols) brings The Clash into Polydor Studios with Guy Stevens at the controls to record demos. These numbers were `Career Opportunities', `White Riot', `Janie Jones', `London's Burning' and `1977'.

18 November 1976

The Clash play Nag's Head, High Wycombe, supporting Clayson & The Argonauts.

29 November 1976

The Clash play Lancaster Polytechnic, Coventry. Terry Chimes has already told the band he intends to quit. They have been rehearsing drummers in between last few gigs. This will be Terry's last gig (for the time being) with the band. His replacement, Rob Harper, has come along to this gig who got the nod The Clash were looking for a new drummer for one Bill Broad (Billy Idol) who Rob used to be in a band with (The Rockettes).

A Brief History

December 1976

It looks like The Clash are to sign to Polydor Records who even send them a telegram saying `Good Luck' as they set off on the `Anarchy' tour.

6 December 1976

The Clash play Leeds Polytechnic, the first night of the ill-fated `Anarchy in the UK' tour (originally this date was to be the fourth Anarchy gig), alongside The Sex Pistols, The Damned and The Heartbreakers. Only three of the original Anarchy dates will be played.

9 December 1976

The Clash play Electric Circus, Manchester, second date of `Anarchy' tour, but The Damned are kicked off the tour due to "lack of solidarity".

14 December 1976

The Clash play Castle Cinema, Caerphilly, Wales, a re-scheduled `Anarchy' tour date with The Sex Pistols and The Heartbreakers.

19 December 1976

The Clash play Electric Circus, Manchester for the second time (few venues will book the `Anarchy' tour) with The Sex Pistols and The Heartbreakers.

20 December 1976

Play Winter Gardens, Cleethorpes, with The Sex Pistols and The Heartbreakers.

21 December 1976

Play Woods Centre, Plymouth, the third original `Anarchy' tour date to survive with The Sex Pistols and The Heartbreakers.

22 December 1976

The Clash play their last gig of 1976. Due to all the cancellations of the `Anarchy' tour, the bands were offered a second show at the Woods Centre, Plymouth.

1 January 1977

The Clash kick in the year with a headlining gig at The Roxy Club, Covent Garden, London, alongside Chelsea (then featuring Billy Idol/Tony James). The Clash play two sets. Rob Harper plays his last gig with The Clash. CBS A&R men are also present at this gig ... they have their eye on The Clash.

January 1977

The Clash head off to Beaconsfield, North London, with Julian Temple and Joe's mate, Mickey Foote, to record some more demos. Terry Chimes fills in on drums, they record `London's Burning', `White Riot', `Career Opportunities', `1977' and `Janie Jones' instrumental (see Bootleg Bible `Another History' LP).

25 January 1977

The Clash sign worldwide deal with CBS for £100,000. This is a turn up for the books as up until the eleventh hour, the band think they are still signing to Polydor. Bernie Rhodes decides to go with CBS.

A Brief History

28 January 1977

The Clash enter CBS Studio 3 for three days over the weekend and record `White Riot/1977' with Mickey Foote behind the controls and Terry Chimes behind the drums.

10 February 1977

The Clash start the first of three Thursday-Sunday sessions to record their first LP, again with Mickey Foote at the controls. Terry Chimes again helps out and records LP, but has made up his mind not to be permanent.

February 1977

John Moss (later of Culture Club) takes on the drum chair and waits for band to finish the recording of the LP, but at the eleventh hour decides he does not like the politics of the band and pulls out of job.

11 March 1977

The Clash play warm-up gig for their `White Riot' tour at The Harlesden Coliseum, London, with support from The Buzzcocks, Subway Sect and The Slits. Terry Chimes again sits in on drums.

18 March 1977

`White Riot' single released; it rises to No. 38 in the UK Charts.

8 April 1977

`The Clash', the debut LP, is released in the UK. It will reach No. 12 in the UK Charts, but C.B.S. have refused to release it in America.

9 April 1977

Capital Radio EP N.M.E. freebie released (see Capital Radio chapter).

April 1977

After auditioning over 200 drummers, Nicky `Topper' Headon is chosen. He is an old face, having auditioned already for `London SS'. Mick Jones bumps into him at a Kink's gig and invites him along to audition.

April 1977

On listening to The Clash's first LP, Bob Marley and Lee `Scratch' Perry record `Punky Reggae Party'. Nice.

26 April 1977

The Clash shot promo film of two tracks `White Riot' and `London's Burning' to mark arrival of Topper Headon in Dunstable, Bedfordshire.

13 May 1977

`Remote Control' released, but not to the band's wishes. The B-side is from the above session Dunstable. The single did not chart.

May 1977

Sebastian Conran, Celia Perry, Al McDowell and Frothler, art school friends, open short-lived shop called `Pollocks' to sell `art clothing' at 271 Brixton Road. On closing, Bernie Rhodes uses

A Brief History

some CBS money to start `Upstarts' with Sebastian to market and sell Clash clothing.

9 May 1977

The Clash play `White Riot' show at The Rainbow Theatre, London, with The Jam, Subway Sect and The Slits. The place gets wrecked by fans. Punk gets out of the clubs into the theatre. The `White Riot' tour makes a £28,000 loss.

10 June 1977

Joe and Topper are fined £5 in London for spraying `Clash' outside Dingwalls.

11 June 1977

Joe and Topper have to travel to Newcastle and are detained overnight for failure to appear in Newcastle Court on 10 June for nicking pillowcases. They are fined £100.

23 September 1977

`Complete Control' released (see Single chapter). It makes No. 28 in UK Charts.

October-November 1977

`Get out of Control' Tour (see Gig Guide), supported on tour by Richard Hell and The Voidoids. Half-way through tour, Rodent (Clash roadie) leaves to work with Johnny Rotten. He is replaced by Johnny Green. Rodent goes on to star in `Punk in London' film.

17 February 1978

`Clash City Rockers' is released. The Clash return from foreign trip to hear the single has been vari-speeded up. Mickey Foote is sacked. Every version since the single has been the normal speed version. No. 38 in UK Charts.

February 1978

Sessions cancelled for follow-up LP, due to Joe getting hepatitis.

March 1978

The Clash enter Marquee Studios to record demos and B-sides.

March 1978

Dave Mingay and Jack Hazan (film makers) meet Ray Gange (Clash fan). They decide to make a film based around his connection with The Clash, etc ... they call it` Rude Boy'.

March 1978

The Clash perform `Tommy Gun' on BBC2's Something Else show.

30 March 1978

Simonon and Headon are arrested in Camden Town, London for shooting racing pigeons with air guns - fined £800. `Guns, guns ... guns on the roof. Guns, guns make to shoot'.

30 April 1978

The Clash headline `Anti-Nazi League Carnival' gig at Victoria Park, Hackney, organised by Rock against Racism. Top show!!

April-May 1978

Band record with American producer, Sandy Pearlman, in Basing Street Studios, CBS Studios and Utopia Studios.

A Brief History

16 June 1978

`White Man in Hammersmith Palais' released (see section). No. 32 in UK Charts.

8 July 1978

Strummer and Simonon are arrested and fined (£25 and £50) for being drunk and disorderly after Apollo Show in Glasgow.

July-August 1978

The Clash play `Out on Parole' tour (see Gig Guide).

September 1978

Bernie Rhodes announces two Roxy Theatre shows starting on 9 September, but Joe and Mick are in America working on LP; they are not happy.

21 October 1978

Bernie Rhodes is sacked as Manager. Replaced by Caroline Coon (Melody Maker journalist).

25/26 October 1978

Re-scheduled shows at Roxy Theatre, Harlesden, London.

10 November 1978

`Give 'em enough Rope' LP is released. It debuts the UK Charts at No. 2 (see LP chapter).

24 November 1978

`Tommy Gun' single released (see chapter), their biggest selling single yet, reaching No. 19 in UK Charts.

November 1978-January 1979

`Sort it Out' tour (see Gig Guide).

19 December 1978

The Clash play Music Machine, London, a benefit for Sid Vicious Defence Fund, as he has killed(?) his girlfriend, Nancy Spungen, in Chelsea Hotel, New York.

23 February 1979

`English Civil War' single released. It will make No. 25 in UK Charts.

February 1979

Group begins 8-date North American tour with Bo Diddley as support. US leg of tour dubbed `Pearl Harbour 79' opening at New York's Palladium.

March 1979

Johnny Green and Baker (Topper's drum roadie) find new rehearsal place for group - Vanilla Studios, Pimlico, London. They start to record third LP.

7 April 1979

`Give 'em enough Rope' (The Clash's first LP release in US, see chapter) makes No. 128 in US Charts.

A Brief History

April 1979

Johnny Green loses `London Calling' tapes on London Underground.
Back to square one...

April 1979

The Clash perform `English Civil War' and `Hate and War' on ITV's Alright Now show

11 May 1979

`Cost of Living' EP released, reaches No. 22 in UK Charts. Caroline Coon is informed her services are no longer required.

26 July 1979

The Clash's first album gets a US release, though modified from UK version (see chapter). It will climb to No. 126 in US Charts.

26 July 1979

Also sees release of The Clash's first US single, `I fought the Law'.

August 1979

Group record 12 songs in three days with Guy Stevens at the controls.

September 1979

Sees the arrival of Kosmo Vinyl (Stiff Records' PR man) to The Clash camp. This connection brings with it Blackmill Management, Ian Dury & The Blockhead's managers, Peter Jenner and Andrew King. With new management, the Clash hit the States for second tour titled `Clash take the Fifth' (being Mickey Gallagher of Blockheads on keyboards), supported by The Undertones and various US bands - Sam and Dave, Screamin' Jay Hawkins, Lee Dorsey, Joe Ely and `The Cramps'.

7 December 1979

`London Calling' single released. It will reach No. 11 in UK Charts.

14 December 1979

`London Calling' double LP released. It will climb UK Charts to No. 9 (see chapter).

27 December 1979

The Clash co-headline second of four benefit concerts for Kampuchea at Hammersmith Odeon, London.

January 1980

`London Calling' LP released. It reaches No. 27 in US Charts.

January-February 1980

`16 Tons' tour named after Tennessee Ernie Ford's `16 Tons' single, `16 Tons and what do I get, another day older and deeper in debt'. Similarities to The Clash/CBS situation.

12 February 1980

`Train in Vain' (Stand by Me), Clash's second single in US. Released it will reach No. 23 in US Charts.

A Brief History

11 March 1980

Paul Simonon takes the part in a Canadian film shot in Vancouver alongside Steve Jones/Paul Cook (Sex Pistols); the film is called `All Washed Up'.

15 March 1980

`Rude Boy' film opens at Prince Charles Cinema, London.

March 1980

Johnny Green leaves the fold to work with Joe Ely.

May 1980

Joe Strummer arrested after smashing his guitar over the head of a violent member of the audience in Hamburg, Germany. He is released after alcohol test proves negative.

August 1980

The Clash begin recording a self-produced LP in Electric Ladyland Studios, New York. Mick Jones produces Ellen Foley's (his current girlfriend) LP (see chapter).

8 August 1980

`Bankrobber' is finally released after much record company debate. In the end, released to combat flood of Dutch import copies; reaches No. 12 in UK Charts.

November 1980

10" mini album `Black Market Clash' released in the States (see chapter). Peaks at No. 74 in US Charts.

21 November 1980

`The Call Up', anti-draft single released; it makes No. 40 in UK Charts.

November 1980

Blackhill Management Services dispensed with.

12 December 1980

Triple LP `Sandinista' released (see chapter); reaches No. 19 in UK Charts.

January 1981

Joe insists on the reinstatement of Bernie Rhodes as Manager.

January 1981

`Sandinista' LP released; it will make No. 24 in US Charts.

16 January 1981

`Hitsville UK' single released; peaks at No. 56 in UK Charts.

17 February 1981

`Hitsville UK/Police on my Back', The Clash's third US single released.

A Brief History

27 March 1981

`The Magnificent Seven' 12" EP released in the States (see chapter).

10 April 1981

`The Magnificent Seven' released; it will reach No. 34 in UK Charts.

May 1981

Bernie Rhodes suggests a promotional plan to play `Magnificent Seven' gigs at Bonds Casino in New York (28 May-5 June). The 4,000 capacity is reduced after first night by City Fire Brigade to 1,750 people. The Clash will end up playing 16 gigs here to compensate fans.

20 November 1981

`This is Radio Clash' released; it will make No. 47 in UK Charts.

25 November 1981

`This is Radio Clash' released in the US (see chapter).

December 1981

Topper caught at Heathrow Airport smuggling Heroin; fined £500. Subject for the song `First Night Back in London'.

January 1982

Mick Jones presents 15-track final mixes of next LP. Band thinks it's way too long and rejects it. Band head off on first tour of the Far East playing Japan, New Zealand, Australia, Hong Kong and Thailand.

March 1982

Group return to London with producer Glyn Johns to sort LP out (see chapter).

21 April 1982

Joe goes missing just before the announced 19-date `Know your Rights' tour.

23 April 1982

`Know your Rights' single released; it will reach No. 43 in UK Charts.

14 May 1982

`Combat Rock' LP released. It will rise to No. 2 in the UK Charts.

17 May 1982

Joe is found in Paris by Kosmo Vinyl. History tell us it was a publicity stunt instigated by Bernie Rhodes. Same day Topper quits the band. Terry Chimes again steps in and band sets off to tour the US.

5 June 1982

`Combat Rock' LP released in the US. Delayed by The Clash's insistence. `Home Taping is Killing Music' is removed from back of sleeve. The LP reaches No. 7 in US Charts, selling over a million copies.

A Brief History

10 June 1982
`Should I stay or should I go' released in US. It will climb to No. 45 in US Charts (see chapter).

11 June 1982
`Rock the Casbah' released; it will reach No. 30 in UK Charts.

2 July 1982
Topper Headon is remanded on bail in London charged with stealing a bus stop and receiving stolen property.

17 September 1982
`Should I stay or should I go' released in UK, making No. 17 in Charts.

22 September 1982
The Clash are invited to support The Who on eight stadium farewell shows including two gigs at Shea Stadium, New York.

9 October 1982
The Clash appear on US Saturday Night Live Show. The play `Should I stay or should I go' and `Straight to Hell'.

27 November 1982
The Clash play Jamaica World Music Festival.

January 1983
`Rock the Casbah' hits No. 8 in US Charts.

February 1983
Terry Chimes leaves band after tour.

April 1983
After auditioning over 300 applicants, The Clash find a drummer in 23 year old Pete Howard from Bath band Cold Fish.

28 April 1983
The Clash headline US Festival in Glen Helen Regional Park, Los Angeles. They are to be paid US$500,000.

20 July 1983
`Should I stay or should I go' re-issued in the States; reaches No. 50.

10 September 1983
Press statement "Joe Strummer and Paul Simonon have decided that Mick Jones should leave the group".

November 1983
Guitarists Vince White and Nick Sheppard are added to the band.

A Brief History

January 1984

New Clash line-up announced - "A whole new Clash era is underway".

January 1984

Mick Jones and Topper Headon have The Clash assets frozen.

February 1984

8-date `Out of Control' tour of Eire and UK takes place.

March 1984

Second leg of tour ends with five nights at Brixton Academy, supported by The Pogues.

March-May 1984

The Clash tour the US - shows not selling out ...

September 1984

Four Italian shows played in support of the `Communist Party'.

6/7 December 1984

The Clash play Benefit Shows at Brixton Academy London in support of the Miners Strike Fund.

May 1985

The Clash play busking tour in UK (see Gig Guide).

29 June 1985

The Clash play Rocksene, Finland.

13 July 1985

The Clash play Roskilde Festival, Denmark.

27 August 1985

The Clash play last ever show at Antic Panathinaikon in Athens, Greece.

September 1985

`This is England' 7" released; reaches No. 24 in UK Charts.

November 1985

`Cut the Crap' album released; it will reach No. 16 in UK Charts and No. 88 in US Charts (see chapter).

23 November 1985

N.M.E. carries a news report - "Nick, Vince and Pete have left the band".

CLASH R.I.P.

White Riot

White Riot / 1977
UK 7"S CBS 5058
Release date - 18/3/1977
Sleeve - Pink lettering on green and white picture sleeve
Label - Black lettering on orange and yellow background

The single was recorded at CBS's Studio 3. Terry Chimes features on drums. Their debut single

(A)

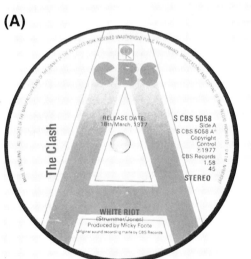

(B)

(A)
Promotional Label
Black lettering on white background, orange `A' on label
(B)
Issue Label
Black lettering on orange and yellow background

Being on a major label for the duration of their career saw each release getting a promotional copy before the issue copy. Except Bankrobber & Magnificent Seven 7" releases (see chapters)

White Riot / 1977
Spanish 7" S CBS 5058
Release date - 1977
Sleeve - **Front** Orange writing on black & white photo green surround;
Back Black lettering on white background
Label - Black lettering on orange and yellow background as UK, but push-out middle

The Spanish sleeve for White Riot uses the first LP sleeve as its cover and advertises the album on the back cover with track listing as well.

White Riot

White Riot / 1977
Italian 7" S CBS 5058
Release date - 1977
Sleeve - **Front** Pink and black lettering on black & white background with pink edging;
Back Black lettering on white background Label - Black lettering on orange background, push-out middle

The Italians used what would be the UK front sleeve for The Clash's third single in the UK for their version of White Riot.

White Riot / 1977
Yugoslavian 7" S CBS 5058/JUS.N.N4 201
Release date - 1977
Sleeve - **Front** Pink and black lettering on green and white picture sleeve;
Back Grey and green lettering on green and white background
Label - Black lettering on orange and yellow background

What makes the Yugoslavian release of White Riot unique is the use of the classic first album review quote "If you don't like The Clash, you don't like Rock'n'Roll" written across the backsleeve ... nice!! Also, train-spotters track titles written on front sleeve.

Other Releases

White Riot /1977
German 7" S CBS 5058
Sleeve - same as UK
(also came as Promo BLITZ information promo sleeve)

White Riot /1977
Australian 7" S CBS 5058
Sleeve - white lettering on blue tinted picture,white boarder around sleeve

White Riot /1977
Holland 7" S CBS 5058
Sleeve - same as UK (some with Punk sticker)

Capital Radio

Capital Radio / Interview/Listen
UK 7" NME Freebie (CL1)
Release date - 9/4/1977
Sleeve - Black & white cover
Label - Black lettering on white background

This version of Capital Radio would not see another release until 1980s 'Black Market Clash' USA 10" LP. But they recorded a new version of this classic for the `Cost of Living' EP in 1979.

(A)

(A)
A-Side Label (shown here)
1. The A-side consists of an interview with Tony Parsons on the London Underground
2. Capital Radio

B Side Label
1. Listen: A Clash instrumental with part of the interview spoken over the top
2. Interview: Further extracts

If there was a Red Sticker attached to the inner sleeve of your copy of the first Clash LP (10,000 stickers were printed), you could send off with a coupon printed in the NME for this 7" release. It contained a Tony Parsons interview with Strummer/Jones on the London Underground. The cover is a picture from the interview. The back sleeve was to contain pictures of graffiti sprayed outside the Capital Radio building on Euston Road by Joe Strummer and Rodent saying `White Riot', but was withdrawn in case of legal action.

Promo sticker stating
Capital Radio … 'In tune with nothing' Nice!

REMOTE CONTROL

**Remote Control /
London's Burning (Live)**
UK 7" S CBS 5293
Release date - 13/5/1977
Sleeve - Red Lettering on black
& white sleeve

The promotional copies of this single carried a studio version of London's Burning as its B-side. The live B-side was recorded during a live video shot for 'White Riot / London's Burning' in Dunstable, Bedfordshire in May 1977.

(A)
Promotional Label
Black lettering on white background, orange `A' on label.

(B)
Issue Label
Black lettering on orange and yellow background

(A)

(B)

Their first LP cover shot is used for their second single release which is put out against their wishes and which they will let the world know about on their next 45 `Complete Control'. Mick Jones takes over lead vocal on their second single release. Maybe the group were right in their protests as the track fails to chart.

Other Releases

**Remote Control/London's
Burning (Studio Version)**
Holland 7" S CBS 5293
Release date - 1977
Sleeve - same as UK

**Remote Control /
London's Burning (Live)**
Irish 7" S CBS 5293
Release date - 1977
No sleeve -
Red/ black label

Complete Control

**Complete Control /
City of the Road**
UK 7" S CBS 5664
Release date - 23/9/1977
Sleeve - **Front** Black lettering
on black & white picture on
pink surround;
Back Pink lettering
on black & white background.

The Clash brought in Lee Perry to help Mickey Foote produce their third single. It makes No. 28 in the UK Charts.

(A)

(B)

(A) Promotional Label
Black lettering on white background, orange `A' on label.

(B) Issue Label
Black lettering on orange and
yellow background

The A-side deals with the band's discontentment with their label over choice of releases and their lack of control over their career. The press gave the group a hard time over this, saying there were bigger issues than worrying about getting your mates in free to your gigs or not.

Other Releases

Complete Control/ City of the Dead
Yugoslavian 7" S CBS 5664
Release date - 1977
Sleeve - same as UK

Complete Control/ City of the Dead
German 7" S CBS 5664
Release date - 1977
Sleeve - same as UK

Complete Control/ City of the Dead
Holland 7" S CBS 5664
Release date - 1977
Sleeve - same as UK

**Complete Control /
City of the Dead**
Spanish 7" S CBS 5664
Sleeve - **Front** Pink and white
writing over colour picture of
the group;
Back black lettering
on white background
Label - Black lettering on
orange and yellow background,
with push-out middle

This classic Spanish sleeve uses an early colour shot of the band showing Strummer with his short-lived orange hairstyle.

Clash City Rockers

Clash City Rockers / Jail Guitar Doors

UK 7" S CBS 5834
Release date - 17/2/1978
Sleeve - Pink writing with black & white pictures on blue background

Both tracks were new releases and were not included on The Clash's next LP `Give 'em Enough Rope'. Although the B-side was a re-working of a 101'ers track with new verses written and sung by Mick Jones. Citing three name checks in the songs verses Wayne (Kramer), Pete (Peter Green), & Micks beloved Keith (Richards).It reaches No. 38 in the UK Charts.

(A)
Promotional Label
Black lettering on white background, orange `A' on label.

(B)
Issue Label
Black lettering on orange and yellow background

(A)

(B)

Other Releases

Clash City Rockers / Jail Guitar Doors

Italian 7" S CBS 5834
Release date - 1978
Sleeve - same as UK

Clash City Rockers / Jail Guitar Doors

Holland 7" S CBS 5834
Release date - 1978
Sleeve - same as UK

Clash City Rockers / Jail Guitar Doors

German 7" S CBS 5834
Release date - 1978
Sleeve - same as UK

The A-side, a riff driven reply to the press stating you "better leave town if you only want to knock us". Mickey Foote (Clash sound man/ producer) was given the sack on Mick/Joe's return from a US trip to find Mickey had vari-speeded the track (making it sound faster) and put this version out. All future versions on `Best of', etc. are normal speed.

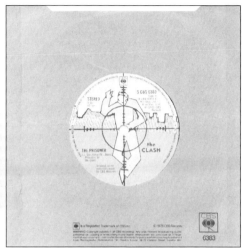

White Man in Hammersmith Palais / The Prisoner
UK 7" S CBS 6383
Release date - 16/6/1978
Sleeve - Die-cut sleeve came in four colours - green, blue, pink and yellow - with black lettering

The Clash produced both sides of this classic 7" and Mick Jones sings the B-side cut. Both cuts were non-LP tracks, which reached No. 32 in the UK Charts.

(A)

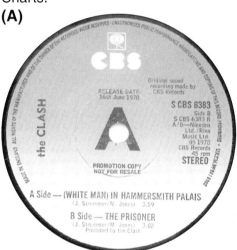

(B)

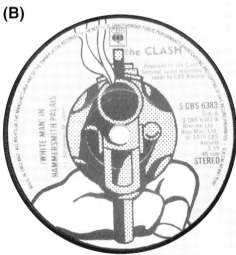

(A) Promotional Label
One side:- Black Lettering on orange/ yellow label with black 'A' (shown).
Otherside Gun picture on green background black 'A'.
(B) Issue Label
Front Black lettering on green background (gun picture);
Back Black lettering on green background (target picture)

CBS printed a special label for The Clash's sixth single showing a gun firing on one side, and a target on the B-side.

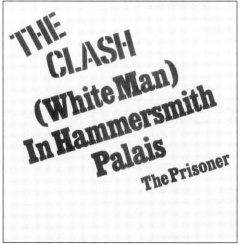

White Man in Hammersmith Palais / The Prisoner
Holland 7" CBS 6383
Release date - 1978
Sleeve - Black lettering on pink background
Label - Black lettering on orange/yellow background

The Holland release used a full pink sleeve as opposed to the UK die-cut sleeve.

Tommy Gun

Tommy Gun /
1-2 Crush on You
UK 7" S CBS 6788
Release date - 24/11/1978
Sleeve - Yellow and red letter-
ing on blue background with
black & white pictures

`Tommy Gun', their biggest selling single so far reaches No. 19 in the UK Charts.

(A) Promotional Label
Black lettering on white background, orange `A' on label.

(B)Issue Label
Black lettering on orange and
yellow background

(A)

(B)

`Tommy Gun', The Clash's seventh and most political statement to date, is released to coincide with their second LP `Give 'em enough Rope'. The B-side is a non-LP cut, `1-2 Crush on You', an early Mick Jones song which he takes lead vocals on, the third single in a row where Mick sings the B-side.

USA producer Sandy Pearlman produces the A-side. The B-side stems from `The Marquee Tapes' that the band produced but CBS were not happy with, so they drafted in `Sandy Pearlman' hopefully to help break The Clash into the USA.

Other Releases
Tommy Gun /
1-2 Crush on You
Australian 7"
CBS BA222478
No picture sleeve.

Tommy Gun /
1-2 Crush on You
New Zealand 7"
CBS BA222478
No picture sleeve.

English Civil War

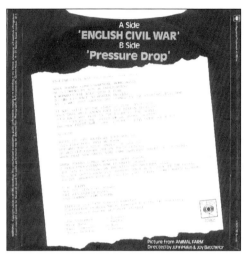

**English Civil War /
Pressure Drop**
UK 7" S CBS 7082
Release date - 23/2/1979
Sleeve - **Front** Blue lettering
on colour carton picture;
Back Blue and black lettering
on black & white background

The sleeve is a still from the picture `Animal Farm'. The A-side is a version of the traditional song `When Johnny comes marching home'. The B-side, The Clash's version of the Toots & The Maytals classic `Pressure Drop'. This, their second single from `Give 'em enough Rope' LP, reached No. 25 in the UK

(A)

(B)

A) Promotional Label
Black lettering on white background, orange `A' on label.

B) Issue Label
Black lettering on orange and yellow background

**Other Releases
English Civil War /
Pressure Drop**
Irish 7" S CBS 7082
Release date - 23/2/1979
No sleeve
Red / Black label

1979 also saw 'White Riot' - 'English Civil War' 7" singles inclusive being re-issued with these original picture sleeves.

**English Civil War /
Pressure Drop**
German 7" CBS S 7082
Release date - 1979
Sleeve - **Front** Black lettering
on red, blue and yellow tinted
sleeve;
Back white and black
lettering on black & white background
Label - Black lettering on
orange background (push-out
centre)

This German release used the `Give 'em enough Rope' LP sleeve for its cover.

Cost Of Living EP

The Cost of Living EP
UK 7"S CBS 7324
Release date - 11/5/1979
Sleeve - Red, yellow and blue gatefold sleeve, with pink and black & white inner sleeve

Four-track EP
Side 1 I fought the Law / Groovy Times
Side 2 Gates of the West / Capital Radio

This EP features a cover version of Bobby Fullers' `I fought the Law' with two `Give 'em Enough Rope' outtakes - `Groovy Times' and `Gates of the West' - and a new recorded version of`Capital Radio'. Plus Fifth unlisted track 'Cost of Living' Radio advert. When it was released, it reached No. 22 in the UK Charts.

(A) Promotional Two-Track Label
I fought the Law / Gates of the West
Black lettering on white background, orange `A' on label

(B) Issue Label
Black lettering on grey and white background

(A)

(B)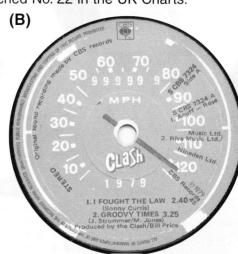

(C) Inner Sleeve
One side Black & white collage of Joe, Mick Topper playing table football,
other side lyrics to `Groovy Times' dropped in with Spanish writings in black lettering on pink background

(D) Cost of Living EP
Holland 7" CBS 7324
Same as UK but not G/ F and with tracks written on front panel. This is the only different sleeve

(C)

(D)

UK sleeve spells Paul Simonon's name wrong on sleeve!!!

I fought the Law /White Man in Hammersmith Palais

I fought the Law / White Man in Hammersmith Palais

Japanese 7" EPIC 06.05.74
Release date - 1979
Sleeve - Insert with black lettering in pink and yellow strips over black & white picture; lyrics to both tracks on other side; record comes in Epic Japan company sleeve
Label - Black lettering on blue background

This Japanese release saw the 'White Man in Hammersmith Palais' single being culled together with one track, `I fought the Law' from the `Cost of Living' EP.

Other Releases

I fought the Law / White Man in Hammersmith Palais

New Zealand 7" B.A. 222539
Release date - 1979
No picture sleeve

I fought the Law / White Man in Hammersmith Palais

Australian 7" B.A. 222539
Release date - 1979
No picture sleeve

I fought the Law / White Man in Hammersmith Palais

USA 7" EPIC 50738
Release date - 24/7/1979
No picture sleeve
The Clash's first US single release.

Released to promote `The Story of The Clash' Volume 1 LP. Also came as a 12" and CD single. (see notes on right)

I fought the Law / City of the Dead / 1977 (Re-issue)

UK 7" re-issue CBS (Clash 1)
Release date - 1988
Sleeve - **Front** silver lettering on blue background
Label - White lettering on blue background; One side Strummer head shot; Other side M Jones head shot

I fought the Law / City of the Dead / Police on my Back / 48 Hours

UK CD Single CBS (Clash SC1)
Release date - 1988
Sleeve - As 7" except yellow background instead of blue

LONDON CALLING

**London Calling /
Armagideon Time**

UK 7" S CBS 8087
Release date - 7/12/1979
Sleeve:- Came in two colours
1)Red front / yellow back
2)Green front / red back - over
black & white picture

The Clash's eighth single is the title track of their double LP `London Calling'.  The B-side is a reggae cover version of Willi Williams' `Armagideon Time'. The sleeve is a pastiche of the1950s style HMV 78s worked in with modern records. Notice the record titles on the sleeve are Elvis, Beatles, Dylan, Stones, Sex Pistols and Clash. Reaches No. 11 in the UK Charts.

A) Promotional Label
Black lettering on white background,orange 'A' on label

B) Issue Label
Black lettering on white background

**London Calling /
Armagideon Time /
Justice Tonight /
Kick it over**

UK 12" S CBS 12 8087
Release date - 7/12/1979
Sleeve - **Front** Black and
yellow lettering on black &
white background;
Back Black and red
lettering on black & white
background

This was The Clash's first 12" single release. It came with the standard ver-sions of the A- and B-side, plus two dub versions of `Armagideon Time'. Also released as a 12" in Holland and Australia.

LONDON CALLING

**London Calling /
Armagideon Time**
Spanish 7" CBS 8087
Release date - 1979
Sleeve - **Front** Pink, green and
white lettering on black & white
picture;
Back black lettering
on white background
Label - Black lettering on
orange background (push-out
centre)

The Spanish sleeve uses the `London Calling' LP sleeve for the cover. The
back cover has the lyrics to `London Calling'.

**London Calling /
Armagideon Time**
Japanese 7" EPIC 06.05.85
Release date - 1979
Sleeve - **Insert front** Pink,
green, white and blue lettering
on black & white picture;
Insert back
Black lettering on white back-
ground; record comes in EPIC
Japan Company sleeve
Label - Black lettering on blue
background

Re-issues

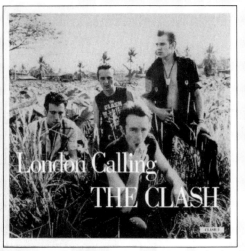

**London Calling /
Brand New Cadillac /
Rudie Can't Fail**
UK 7" Re-issue Clash 2
Release date - 1988
Sleeve - White lettering on
peach coloured sleeve
Label - White lettering on
peach coloured background;
Label one Strummer head shot;
Label two M Jones head shot

`London Calling' was the second single to be released to promote `The Story of The Clash'
Volume 1 LP. It came as a 7"/CD in a round metal tin and a limited 7" box shown on next
page CD tracks - `London Calling', `Clampdown', `Call up', `London's Burning Live'

LONDON CALLING

London Calling /
Brand New Cadillac /
Rudie Can't Fail
UK 7" Re-issue Clash B2
Release date - 1988
Sleeve - As previous page
Label - As previous page
Box containing - 7" single; 2
badges; poster

London Calling /
Brand New Cadillac
UK 7" Columbia 656946 7
Release date - 1991
Sleeve - **Front** White lettering
in pink box on black & white
picture;
Back White writing in
purple circle on pink back-
ground
Label - Black lettering on red
background

This is a later edition to re-promote `Story of The Clash Volume 1',
Also came as 4 track CD. Tracks:- London calling / Brand new Cadillac /
Rudie can't fail / Street parade. Blue wash over picture (clash 2)

Also released
Australian 5-track 12"
`London Calling',
`Magificent Dance',
`This is Radio Clash',
`Rock the Casbah',
`This is England'.

London calling/
Armagideon time
Holland 7"
Release date:- 1977
Sleeve:- as UK
Yellow front / red back

London Calling /
This is Radio Clash /
Rock The Casbah /
Brand New Cadillac
French Promotional 12"
Columbia Samp 23736
Promo release date - 1991
Sleeve - Red and yellow letter-
ing on blue and black back-
ground
Label - Black lettering on white
background

French Promotional only 12" to
promote `Clash the Singles' CD.

Train in Vain (Stand by Me)

Train in Vain / London Calling
USA 7" EPIC 9-50851
Release date - 12/12/1980
Sleeve - Custom Epic sleeve
Label - White lettering on blue background

USA and Canada went with this coupling as a 7" release, giving The Clash their first US Top 30 hit.

(A)    **(B)**

(A) USA Promotional 10"
Train in Vain 10" AS 749
Promotional release date - 1980

(B) Train in Vain (Stand by Me) / London Calling
USA Promotional 7"

`Train in Vain' had a 10" promo in The States, same track both sides.and a 7" promo coupled with London calling

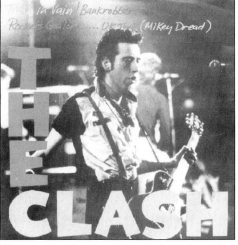 

Train in Vain / Bankrobber / Rockers Galore ... UK Tour
Holland 7" CBS 8370
Release date - 6/1980
Sleeve - Pink and green lettering on black & white picture sleeve
Label - Black lettering on orange and yellow background

This classic track was passed over and not given a UK 7" release, but came out with this sleeve in Holland and Germany (same Cat. No.). Mick Jones cover shot.

Train in Vain /
Bankrobber /
Rockers Galore ... UK Tour
Spanish 7" CBS 8370
Release date - 1980
Sleeve - **Front** Pink and green
lettering on black & white
sleeve;
Back Black lettering on white
background
Label - Black lettering on
orange and yellow background

The Spanish release has a picture of Topper Headon on sleeve.

Train in Vain /
Bankrobber /
Rockers Galore ... UK Tour
Australian 7" EPIC ES 452
Release date - 1980
Sleeve - **Front** White lettering
over pink tinted picture;
Back White lettering over
green tinted picture

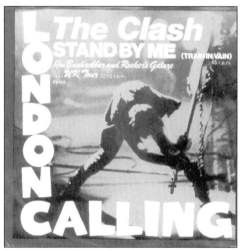

The Australian release uses the `London Calling' LP sleeve of Paul
Simonon for its cover.

Train in Vain /
London Calling
Brazilian 7" EPIC 46014
Release date - 1980
Sleeve - White and pink letter-
ing on black & white wrap-
around sleeve
Label - Black lettering on
orange background

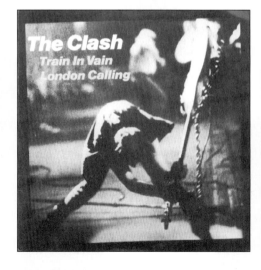 

Train in Vain (Stand by Me)

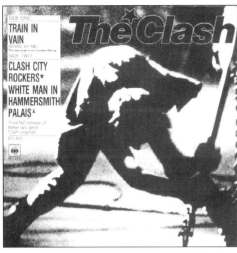

**Train in Vain /
Clash City Rockers /
White Man in
Hammersmith Palais**
New Zealand 7" EPIC ES 452
Release date - 1980
Sleeve - Black lettering on
black & white picture sleeve
Label   White lettering on blue
background

New Zealand put this EP together as `Clash City Rockers/White Man' had
not been released as singles in New Zealand. They use a blown up picture
of Paul Simonon for their cover shot.

Train in Vain
French promo only 7" CBS
PRO 43
Release Date - 1980
Sleeve - Blue lettering on white
background
Label - Black lettering on white
background

The French put out this promo 7" for juke boxes and promotional
purposes.

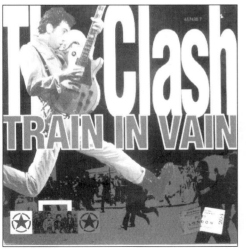

**Train in Vain /
The Right Profile**
Holland 7" Columbia 6574307
Release date - 10/1991
Sleeve - Yellow and red
lettering on black & blue
background
Label - Black & white lettering
on red background

This coupling was released to promote `The Clash, the Singles' CD.
Also came as 4 track picture CD Cat No 657430-2.
Train in vain / Right profile / Groovy times / Gates of the west

Rudie Can't Fail

**Rudie Can't Fail /
Bankrobber /
Rockers Galore ... UK Tour**
Holland 7" CBS 8383
Release date - 6/1980
Sleeve - Pink and green
lettering on black & white
sleeve
Label - Black lettering on
orange and yellow background

Holland really went for the `London Calling' singles push, firstly releasing
`Bankrobber' then `Train in Vain' with `Bankrobber' again, and then `Rudie
Can't Fail' again with `Bankrobber'. Still, at least they finished the set of
sleeves by using Joe Strummer for the sleeve shot (see story below).

(A)

(B)

**Foreign sleeves that make
set of four**

(A) Joe Strummer
Rudie Can't
Fail/Bankrobber/Rockers
Galore ... UK Tour
Holland 7" CBS 8383

(B) Mick Jones
Train in Vain/Rockers Galore ...
UK Tour
Holland 7" CBS 8370

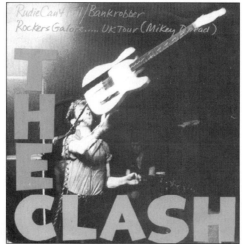

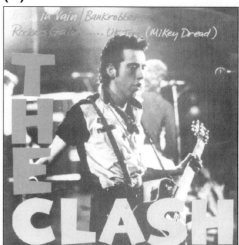

(C) Topper Headon
Train in
Vain/Bankrobber/Rockers
Galore ... UK Tour
Spanish 7" CBS 8370

(C)

(D)

(D) Paul Simonon
Train in Vain/London Calling
Brazilian 7" EPIC (61139238)

CLAMPDOWN

**Clampdown /
Guns of Brixton**
Australian 7" EPIC 486
Release date - 1980
Sleeve - Yellow lettering on
black & white sleeve
Label - Black lettering on blue
background

`Clampdown' got this Australian only 7" release using a stage shot mainly of Topper
Headon and giving Paul Simonon,s `Guns of Brixton' track as its B-side.

Also:

Clampdown / Brand New Cadillac / Spanish Bombs
USA Promotional 10"

Clampdown / Lost in the Supermarket / Card Cheat / London Calling
USA Promotional 12"

Somebody got Murdered

**Somebody got Murdered /
Hitsville UK**
Spanish 7" CBS A 1310
Release date - 1981
Sleeve - **Front** Red lettering
on black & white picture sleeve;
Back Black lettering on white
background
Label - Black lettering on
orange and yellow background

The Spanish release saw this non-single track `Somebody got Murdered'
coupled with `Hitsville UK'. Nice group shot on cover and lyrics of
`Somebody' on back sleeve.

Clash ... The Singles Japanese Box Set

The Clash Singles
Japanese 7" Box Set
EPIC 44-5P-103-110
Release date - 12/1979
Box - Black lettering in red circle on black & white box
Label - Black lettering on orange and yellow background

This Japanese release saw The Clash's first eight 7" singles in their original sleeves being repackaged together in a 7" box set, with colour insert showing sleeves / titles / release dates, and on the other side The Clash's first four Japanese LP releases with pictures / track listings in Japanese. Also two black & white booklets which contain the lyrics in both Japanese and English.

All the sleeves are pretty identical except in texture of paper and the `White Man' sleeve which was not die-cut in the middle (ie. no hole).

The labels are similar to UK labels - black lettering on orange and yellow background, except they carry the Japanese Cat No. 44 5P 103 and each single listed Record 1 ... Record 2, etc. `White Man' has gun label and `London Calling' has the black & white label design.

1) **White Riot /
1977**

2) **Remote Control /
London's Burning (live)**

Record 1

Record 2

Clash ... The Singles Japanese BOX Set

Record 3

Record 4

**3) Complete Control /
The City of the Dead**

**4) Clash City Rockers /
Jail Guitar Doors**

Record 5

Record 6

**5) White Man in
Hammersmith Palais /
The Prisoner**

**6) Tommy gun /
1-2 Crush on you**

Record 7

Record 8

**7) English Civil War /
Pressure Drop**

**8) London Calling /
Armagideon Time**

Bankrobber

Bankrobber /
Rockers Galore ... UK Tour
UK 7" CBS 8323
Release date - 8/ 8/ 1980
Sleeve - Red lettering on black
& white sleeve
Producer - Mickey Dread

 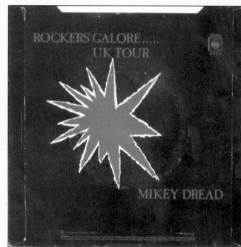

This non-LP track sees The Clash dabbling more with their reggae side, with help from Jamaican DJ Mickey Dread who was touring with the band at this time. Due to a flood of Dutch copies, it was released in the UK and reached No. 12 in the Charts.

Issue Label
Red lettering on black background

This UK 7" didn't come with a demo label due to the demos being cut on 10" acetate only. Reggae style.

Recorded in Pluto Studios, Manchester on 1-2 February 1980 with Mickey Dread at the controls. This was to be the first of a `Clash Singles Bonanza'. Fed up with no air play, they came up with this idea of putting out a series of rapid fire singles, one after the other, until one hit home ...

Bank Robber /
Rockers Galore ... UK Tour
Japanese 7" EPIC 07 5P-116
Release date - 1980
Sleeve - Red lettering on black
& white sleeve
Label - Black lettering on blue
background

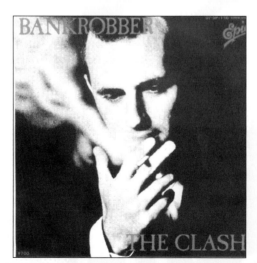 

This Japanese release reverted back to a proper sleeve format with insert inside containing lyrics. Also advertising the aforementioned Japanese 8-single box set.

The Call Up

**The Call Up /
Stop the World**
UK 7" S CBS 9339
Release date - 21/11/1980
Sleeve - Red lettering on black
& white sleeve

The Clash's anti-draft song and first single to be taken from their triple LP `Sandinista' reached No. 40 in the UK Charts.

(A)

(B)

A) Promotional Label
Black lettering on white
background, orange `A' on
label

B) Issue Label
Black lettering on red
background

Other Releases

**The Call Up /
Stop the World**
Australian 7" EPIC E.S. 549

**The Call Up /
Stop the World**
Japanese 7" EPIC 07-5P-127
Release date - 1980
Sleeve - Insert with red lettering on black & white picture;
lyrics on other side; record
comes in Epic Japan Company
sleeve
Label - Black lettering on blue
background

**The Call Up /
Stop the World**
New Zealand 7" EPIC E.S. 549
White lettering on black & white sleeve

The Call Up/Stop the World
Holland 7" CBS 9339
With black & white sticker saying
`The Clash' on front cover

The Call Up 12" EP
Magnificent Dance/Magnificent Seven/Call
Up/Cool Out
US 12" only EPIC 49-02036
Release date - 1981

EPIC decide to use an insert sleeve for this release.
Also Japanese magazine "Music Life" 1980 has free 7" red flexi disc featuring new year messages from The Clash (Paul & Joe), Police, Japan & Cheap Trick. Released around this time.

Hitsville UK

Hitsville UK / Radio One
UK 7" S CBS 9480
Release date - 16/1/1981
Sleeve - Red and black die-cut sleeve

(A) Promotional Label
Black lettering on white background, orange `A' on label

(B) Issue Label
Black lettering on white background

`Hitsville UK' Mick Jones duets with Ellen Foley on this Motown sounding ditty in praise of the independent labels of the UK. The sleeve is a collage of Indie labels - Factory, Rough Trade, Fast, Small Wonder, etc. It peaked in the UK Charts at No. 56.

Other Releases

Hitsville UK / Police on my Back
USA 7" EPIC 19-51013
(no picture sleeve)
Release date - 1981

Hitsville also released in
Holland, Australia and New Zealand (no picture sleeves)

The Magnificent Seven

**The Magnificent Seven /
The Magnificent Dance**
UK 7" CBS A 1133
Release date - 10/4/1981
Sleeve - Brown, grey and black
die-cut sleeve

No promo copy exists for `Magnificent Seven' UK 7" release.

Originally to be titled `Magnificent Seven Rappo-Clappers' playing tribute to the `Sugarhill Gang' New York rap group. The Clash recorded this track in Jimi Hendrix's old studio `Electric Ladyland' in New York City. It takes full advantage of the presence of Norman Watt-Roy (Ian Dury & The Blockheads' bass player) filling in for the absent Paul Simonon away filming at the time (see Brief History).The Clash's first dance-oriented single was given an extra push by being released on 12" format for club exposure which came with same sleeve, same versions (CBS A12 1133). `Magnificent Seven' reaches No. 34 in the UK Charts.

Issue Label
Label - **Side 1** Red lettering on grey background;
Side 2 Red lettering on black & white background

**The Magnificent Seven /
The Magnificent Dance**
French 7" CBS A 1134
Release date - 1981
Sleeve - **Front** White writing on green background (black and red roulette wheel);
Back Black& white
Label - Black lettering on gold background
(injection moulded).

Remixed by Pepe Unidos (Mick Jones). The French release also came as two 12" single versions - same tracks, but: (1) green background on sleeve;
(2) red background on sleeve.

The Magnificent Seven (Special Remix) / The Magnificent Dance
Holland 7" CBS A 1134
Release date - 1981
Sleeve - Green lettering on light green background die-cut sleeve
Label - **Side One** Black, red and white roulette wheel on label; **Side Two** Red lettering on black background

The Holland release of this track had a special remix version for the A-side. Also came as a 12" - same sleeve and tracks.

The Magnificent Seven / Stop the World
Spanish 7" CBS 9513
Release date - 1980
Sleeve - **Front** red lettering on black & white picture background;
Back Black lettering on white background

The Spanish were quick off the mark to promote the `Sandinista' LP using the cover shot of the album with the Spanish title `Los 7 Magnificos' across the top. Also came as a promo labelled version - same sleeve. And as a two track promo 7" The Magnificent Seven / The Magnificent Dance in picture sleeve DJ only (MIZ89)

The Magnificent Seven / The Magnificent Dance
French 7" Columbia 6576397
Release date - 1991
Sleeve - **Front** black lettering on red background (black/red roulette wheel)
Label - Black & white lettering on red background

Released in 1991 to promote `The Story of The Clash Volume 1' LP. Although pressed in Holland, it was made specially for the French market.

Magnificent Seven 12" Story

As `Magnificent Seven' was The Clash's step into the crossover rap/dance area, CBS promoted the 12" single around the world in some countries more so as a promotional release just to get the `Clash' heard in clubland, such as:

Magnificent Seven/ Call Up/ Tommy Gun/ Lost in the Supermarket
Italian Promo only 4-track 12" (PRM 023/4)

Magnificent Seven / Lightning Strikes / One More Time / Over More Time Dub
USA Promo 12" EPIC (XSM 168456)

Magnificent Seven / Adam & The Ants `Dog eat Dog' (side 2)
Spanish Promo only 12"

Magnificent Seven / Call Up
French Promo 12" (SDC54)

Magnificent Seven / Cool Out
USA Promo 12"

B-side, `Cool Out', is an instrumental remixed version of `Call Up' track showing what a powerful track `Call Up' could have been. This remix was by Mick Jones.

Other Releases

Magnificent Dance / Magnificent Seven / The call up /Cool Out 4
US 12" EP Epic 0023
Release Date:- 27 / 3 / 81

This is Radio Clash

**This is Radio Clash /
Radio Clash**
UK 7" CBS A 1797
Release date - 20/11/1981
Sleeve - **Front** Red writing on
silver and black background;
Back black writing on silver
and red background

The much talked of `Radio Station' The Clash would run came to no avail ... so the idea
was put into words on this single. The track' was basically a reworking of Queen's `Another
One Bites the Dust' bass line.`This is Radio Clash' will climb the UK Charts to No. 47.

(A) Promotional Label
Black & white lettering on yellow and black background;
white `A' centre of label

(A)

Issue Label
The same as above, minus the
white `A' centre

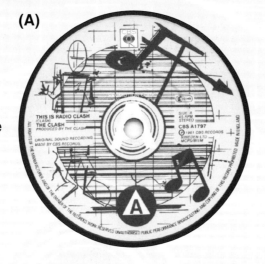

**This is Radio Clash /
Radio Clash /
Outside Broadcast /
Radio 5**
UK 12" CBS A 13 1797
Release date - 4/12/1981

Also Released

**This is Radio Clash
(12" EP only)**
US 12" EPIC 49-02662
Release date -
25/11/1981
This is Radio Clash /
Radio Clash / Outside
Broadcast / Radio 5

This is Radio Clash

This is Radio Clash / Radio Clash
Spanish 7" CBS A 1727
Release date - 1981
Sleeve - **Front** Red writing on silver and black background;
Back Black lettering on white background
Label - Promotional label Black lettering on white background;
Issue label Black lettering on orange background

Notice on the Spanish issue different back sleeve with lyrics, but also advertising other CBS artists ... Adam Ant / Toyah / Herbie Handcock.

This is Radio Clash / Radio Clash
Japanese 7" EPIC 07-5P-164
Release date - 1981
Sleeve - Insert **front** Red and white lettering on silver and black background;
Back Black & white lettering on silver and red background
Label - Black lettering on black and yellow background (as UK)

This Japanese release came with an insert sleeve with the lyrics on the back side of insert.

Other Releases

This is Radio Clash / Radio Clash
Australian 7" EPIC ES 700
Release date - 1981
Same sleeve/label as UK

This is Radio Clash / Radio Clash
Greek 7" CBS 1797
No picture sleeve

Know your Rights

**Know your Rights /
First Night Back in London**
UK 7" CBS A 2309
Release date - 23/4/1982
Sleeve - **Front** Yellow, black
and red writing on red and grey
background

(A) Label
Yellow, red and black writing
(as sleeve) on brown and black
background

(B) Sticker
Round sticker - black writing on
yellow and red background;
came with initial run of 7"

Promotional label same as above with addition of `Promotional copy - not
for sale' written on B-side in silver.

`Know your Rights' - in Clash `speak' "you can protest as long as you don't
protest" - hits the UK Charts at No. 43. This was the first single to be lifted
from the Group's `Combat Rock' album.

Know your Rights

**Know your Rights /
First Night Back in London**
Spanish 7" CBS A-2309
Release date - 1982
Sleeve - **Front** Same as UK;
Back Black lettering on white
background

The Spanish version came as a promotional and issue release. The back sleeve contains lyrics of track (as shown) and advertises the LP it came from `Combat Rock'.

Insert front

Insert back

**Know your Rights /
First Night Back in London**
Japanese 7" EPIC 07-5P-177
Release date - 1982
Sleeve - **Insert front** Yellow,
red, black and white lettering
on red, yellow, grey and black
background (as UK);
Insert Back Yellow and red
lettering on grey and black
background
Label - As UK label

Japanese release came as insert sleeve, lyrics on back side of insert.

Other Releases

**Know your Rights /
First Night Back in London**
Holland 7" CBS 2309
Sleeve - As UK

**Know your Rights /
First Night Back in London**
Italian 7" CBS 2309
Sleeve - As UK

**Know your Rights /
First Night Back in London**
Australian 7" EPIC ES 604
Sleeve - As UK

ROCk the Casbah

**Rock the Casbah /
Long Time Jerk**
UK 7" CBS A-2479
Release date - 11/6/1982
Sleeve - **Front** Yellow and
white lettering on colour pic-
ture;
Back Yellow, red and black
lettering on grey and black
background

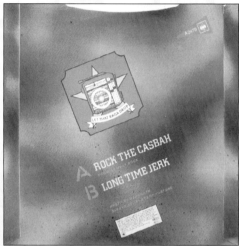

CBS went to town with extra formats for this single. Giving us a 7" picture disc,
as well as 12" release which helped to push it up the UK Charts to No. 30.

(A)

(B)

(A) Label
Red, yellow and black lettering
on grey and black background

(B) Sticker
Set of four stickers on one
sheet came with initial run
of 7".

Promotional label same as above with addition of a small silver 'A' on the
middle of label

**Rock the Casbah /
Long Time Jerk**
UK 7" Picture Disc A11 2479
Release date - 1982
Pictures - A-side same as 7"
sleeve with added green border
background' B-side Black
lettering colour picture with
green border background

Also released

**Rock the Casbah /
Mustapha Dance**
UK 12" CBS A12 2474

The two characters on the sleeve are `The Arab' Bernie Rhodes and `The
Orthodox Jew ' band friend Mark Helfont.

**Rock the Casbah /
Long Time Jerk**
Spanish 7" CBS A-2479
Release date - 1982
Sleeve - **Front** Same as UK;
Back Black lettering on white
background
Label - Black lettering on
orange and yellow background

As usual with Spanish releases, lyrics are printed on back side of sleeve with picture of LP and track listing.

**Rock the Casbah /
Mustapha Dance**
Japanese 7" EPIC 07-SP-191
Release date - 1982
Sleeve - Insert A-side Yellow,
red and white lettering on
picture (as UK); B-side insert
Red lettering on white
background
Label - Black lettering on light
blue background

The Japanese release used `Mustapha Dance' version for its B-side and added the lyrics in both English and Japanese on B-side of insert.

**Rock the Casbah /
Mustapha Dance**
USA 12" EPIC 4903144
Release date - 1982
Sleeve - Same as UK with
silver border
Label - Silver lettering on blue
and black background

Also released
**Rock the Casbah /
Long Time Jerk**
USA 7" EPIC 14-03245
Release date - 1982
Sleeve - EPIC company sleeve
Label - As above

'Rock the Casbah' was the first record to be broadcast on armed forces radio during the Persian Gulf war.

ROCk the Casbah

Rock the Casbah / Red Angel Dragnet

Canadian 7" EPIC 3403245
Release date - 1982
Sleeve - EPIC company sleeve
Label - Silver lettering on blue and black background

The Canadian release saw `Red Angel Dragnet' from the Combat Rock album being used for its B-side. This coupling was used years later on the USA `Hall of Fame' label release.

Other Releases

Rock the Casbah / Long Time Jerk

(release dates 1982)
Came out in Holland, Ireland, Australia & Germany - same sleeve and matrix numbers
Also came out in Greece, New Zealand - no sleeves

Rock the Casbah / Overpowered by Funk

Argentinean 7" Promo only
EPIC 40305 - no sleeve

Rock the Casbah / Mustapha Dance

Re-issue 7" Columbia 6568147
Release date - 1991
Sleeve - Yellow lettering on red tinted picture sleeve
Label - Black and white lettering on red background

Rock The Casbah / Remote Control / Clash City Rockers / London calling

Irish four pack 7"singles in plastic wallet
Release Date:-1982
Label:- Black lettering on orange background

Often mentioned is the unique sleeve for 'London calling' from Ireland. But this was in fact part of a four pack Re-issue set released in Ireland the 'London Calling' sleeve has Paul Simonon on front (as 'London calling' sleeve) & Joe Strummer on back side.
The other 3 sleeves are as U.K.

`Rock the Casbah' was the second single to be re-issued to promote `The Story of The Clash Volume 1' LP. It also came as a 3-track 12"`Rock the Casbah'/ Mustapha Dance/ The Magnificent Dance (sleeve as re-issue7") and 4-track CD in round tin - tracks `Rock the Casbah', `Tommy Gun', `White Man', `Straight to Hell'.

Should I Stay or Should I Go / Straight to Hell

Should I Stay or Should I Go / Straight to Hell
UK 7" CBS A 2646
Release date - 17/9/1982
Sleeve - Front Yellow, red and black lettering on blue and black art sleeve background; **Back** Yellow and red lettering on blue and black art sleeve background (blue snake image)

The third 7" release from the `Combat Rock' LP was this double A-sided single which reached No. 17 in the UK Charts and was their break through single in the US reaching No. 45 in the US Charts. It was then re-issued for the first time in March 1983 in the US and climbed to No 50.

(A) Label
Promotional label shown here - black lettering on white background, orange `A' on label.

(B) Sticker
Limited sticker with initial run of 7" - white lettering in red box, blue snake figure on blue and black background (as back 7" sleeve).

`A' Label                    `B' Sticker

Should I Stay or Should I Go / Straight to Hell
UK 7" Picture Disc CBS A11 2646
Release date - 17/9/1982
Sleeve - Front Picture as 7"; **Back** Red writing on camouflaged background black & white picture of band

CBS used the extra format of 7" picture disc to help push these tracks.

Should I Stay or Should I Go / Straight to Hell
UK 12" CBS A13 2646
Release date - 17/9/1982
Sleeve - As 7" sleeve
Label - Red, yellow and white lettering on black star with green/light green camouflage background

The 12" version came with a Clash `stencil'. Both tracks were the same versions as the 7".

Should I Stay or Should I Go / Cool Confusion
USA 7" EPIC 34-03547
Release date - 24/6/1982
Sleeve - **Front** Yellow and red lettering on blue and green background (faces black & white);
Back Red lettering on blue and green background, yellow star in middle
Label - Silver lettering on blue/dark blue background

As we stated early in this chapter, this was the band's break through single in the USA, reaching No. 45 in the Charts. Helped along by their `The Who' support dates (see Brief History) and EPIC's marketing tools, this single had various formats. Notice the none LP track `Cool Confusion' which was only available as the B-side of this single in Holland / Japan and on this version of US 7".

Should I Stay or Should I Go /
First Night Back in London
USA 7" EPIC 14-03061
Release date - 20/7/1982
Sleeve - Red and black lettering on yellow tinted sleeve
Label - as above

This version came out as a limited edition. Notice the Ronald Reagan picture on sleeve, Should He Stay or Should He Go ... Go.

Should I Stay or Should I Go/ Straight to Hell

Should I Stay or Should I Go / Straight to Hell

Spanish 7" CBS A-2646
Release date - 1982
Sleeve - **Front** Orange and white lettering on colour picture of the band;
Back Black lettering on white background
Label - Black lettering on orange and yellow background

This Spanish release carries a classic picture of the band on the front and lyrics of the track on the back.

Should I Stay or Should I Go / Cool Confusion

Japanese 7" EPIC 07-5P-223
Release date - 1982
Sleeve - **Insert front** Yellow, red and black lettering on blue and green background (graphics black & white), cream border; **Insert back** Black lettering on white background
Label - Black lettering on light blue background

This Japanese release came with an insert sleeve which carries the lyrics of the A-side in English and Japanese. It also uses, as mentioned earlier, the non-LP track `Cool Confusion' as its B-side.

Should I Stay or Should I Go (Clash) / Rush (Big Audio Dynamite II)

Re-issue 7" Columbia 6566677
Release date - 2/3/1991
Sleeve - **Front** White lettering on mauve background;
Back Red and black lettering on colour picture background
Label - Black and white writing on red background

After much disagreement between Strummer and Jones over sponsorship of the product, `Should I Stay or Should I Go' was re-issued through its use in a Levi's TV Ad. It entered the Charts at No. 5 and hit the No.1 spot a week later, giving the Clash their first No1 hit single. It carried a `Big Audio Dynamite II' track as a B-side at the insistence of Mick Jones to help promote his band in the USA.

SHOULD I STAY OR SHOULD I GO

Also came as
Should I Stay or Should I Go /
Rush /
Protex Blue /
Rush (dance mix)l
4 track CD Columbia 656667 2 (in round metal tin).

Should I Stay or Should I Go (Clash) /
Rush (Big Audio Dynamite II) /
Protex Blue (Clash)
12" Columbia 656667 6
Release date - 2/3/1991
Sleeve - same as 7" Re-issue

Also released in the USA

Should I Stay or Should I Go /
Inoculated City
USA 7" EPIC 14-03006
Release date - 10/6/1982
No picture sleeve/same label design as US
Notice different B-side again, this coupling also
released in Canada

Should I Stay or Should I Go
USA 7" ENR 03571
1-sided Promotional only laser etched 7"

Other Important Releases

Should I Stay or Should I Go /
Cool Confusion
Holland 7" CBS A 3166
Release date - 1982
Sleeve - same as USA
Same sleeve and coupling as USA 7"
EPIC 34-03547

Should I Stay or Should I Go /
Straight to Hell
South African 7" CBS 556 5396
No picture sleeve

Should I Stay or Should I Go /
Straight to Hell
Australian 7" EPIC ES 807

Should I Stay or Should I Go
(The Clash) /
Overkill (Men at Work)
Japanese promo only 12" QY3P 90057
Sleeve - picture of Joe/ Mick

Should I Stay or Should I Go...... history tells us this will be the classic Clash line up of
Strummer/ Jones/ Simonon/ Headon's. Last Single release

rpm ... R.I.P. ...

THIS IS ENGLAND

This is England /
Do It Now
UK 7" CBS A 6122
Release date - 9/1985
Sleeve - **Front** Yellow lettering
on colour painted background;
Back Purple and yellow writing
on black & white picture
collage background

(A)

(B)

(A) Label
Front Red lettering on yellow
and black background;
Back Red lettering on black
and white background

(B) Poster Sleeve
Initial copies of 7" came in a
poster fold-out sleeve, as
shown, other side is a colour
picture of group (new line-up).

`This is England' was the only single to be released from the `Cut the Crap' LP. It featured the new Clash line up:

Joe Strummer	(vocals)
Paul Simonon	(bass)
Pete Howard	(drums)
Vince White	(guitar)
Nick Shepperd	(guitar)

Joe now concentrating on vocals. It climbed UK Charts to No. 24. Also came as 3-track 12".

This is England /
Do it Now /
Sex Mad Roar
UK 12" CBS TA 6122
Sleeve - as UK 7" sleeve
Label - as UK 7" layout

This is England

This is England /
Do It Now
Spanish 7" CBS A 6122
Release date - 1985
Sleeve - as UK 7" except
lettering on back in black &
white

Promotional Spanish label shown

Other Notable Releases

This is England /
Do It Now
Holland 7" CBS A 6122
Release date -
Sleeve - as UK
Notable difference is the A-side
of `This is England `is a **dub**
version.

This is England /
Do It Now
US 12" EPIC EAS:2230
Canadian 12"
EPIC 12 CDN-234

This is England /
Do It Now
Australian/New Zealand 7"
EPIC E.S. 1069
Australian/New Zealand 12"
EPIC E.S. 12155

This is England /
Do It Now
Japanese 7" EPIC 07-5P-383
Release date - 1985

By the time the album/single had hit the streets, The Clash were no
more, Joe/Paul being disillusioned with the way the band were going
and by the poor reviews they had received (see `Cut the Crap' in LP
chapter)Called it a day. This track has been overlooked but in retro-
spect stands up as a fine single.

Return to Brixton

**Return to Brixton /
The Guns of Brixton**
UK 7" CBS 656072-7
Release date - 7/1990
Sleeve - Black & white lettering
on yellow and pink background
Label - Black & white lettering
on red background

Released in response to Beatmasters No. 1. Track `Dub be Good to Me' which used Paul's
baseline as its backdrop With additional remix production by Jeremy Healy, this version reached
No. 57 in the UK Charts. Backed with the original version `Guns of Brixton' as its B- side.

Issue Label
As shown.

**Return to Brixton /
Return to Brixton (Dub)**
UK 12" CBS 656072-6
Release date - 7/1990
Sleeve - Black & white lettering
on yellow and pink background
Label - Black & white lettering
on red background

**Return to Brixton /
The Guns of Brixton**
UK Promo 12" CBS XPR 1539

This updated version of `Guns of Brixton' called `Return to Brixton' also
came as a 12" using a dub version of the title track as its B-side.

COLLaborations

Tymon Dogg
Lose this Skin /
Indestructible
UK 7" Ghost Dance GHO-1
Release date - 6/1981
Sleeve:- Brown lettering on
brown and white picture
background.
Label:- Black lettering on green
and white background.

Joe's mate, Tymon Dogg from 101'ers days, gets a hand from The Clash for this release. The track also got aired on the `Sandinista' LP recorded in New York. Ellen Foley sings on both tracks and the B-side features on the `Spirit of St Louis' LP (see LP section).

Futura 2000
The Escapades of Futura
2000
UK 7" Celluloid CYZ-7-104
Release date - 5/1983
Sleeve - yellow and white
lettering on colour sleeve
Label - Black lettering on white
background

Co-written with Mick Jones, this collaboration with Futura 2000, a New York graffiti/ DJ artist who sprayed the backdrops on The Clash's New York `Bonds Club' shows. All The Clash play on this track. It shows the seeds of Mick Jones' `Big Audio Dynamite Group' were sown around this time. Also available on 12"

Janie Jones and The Lash
House of the Ju-Ju Queen /
Sex Machine
UK 7" Big Beat NS91-A
Release date - 12/1983
Sleeve - Red and black
lettering on colour sleeve
Label - Red and black lettering
on blue and white background

As a payback for their first album, opening track `Janie Jones', Joe, Mick and Paul (The Lash) played on this single. The A-side was written and produced by Joe Strummer.

White Riot (Spanish) page 19

Complete Control (Spanish) page 23

English Civil War (German) page 27

I Fought the Law/White man (Japanese) page 29

London Calling (Japanese) page 31

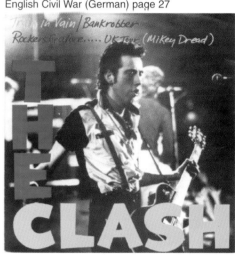

Train in Vain (Dutch) page 33

Train in Vain (Spanish) page 34

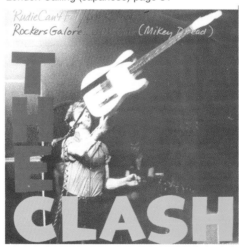

Rudie Can't Fail (Dutch) page 36

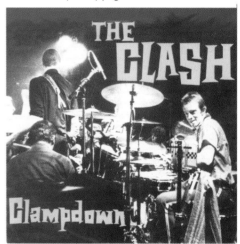

Clampdown (Australian) page 37

Somebody Got Murdered (Spanish) page 37

The Magnificent Seven (Spanish) page 44

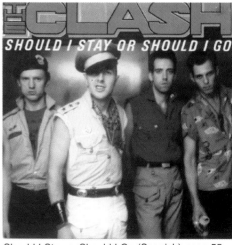

Should I Stay or Should I Go (Spanish) page 55

White Riot page 19

Remote Control page 22

Complete Control page 23

English Civil War page 27

Cost of Living E.P. page 28

London Calling page 30

The Magnificent Seven page 43

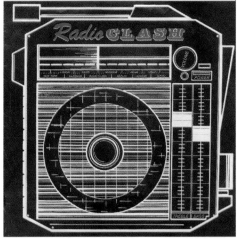

This is Radio Clash page 46

Know your Rights page 48

The Clash LP page 61

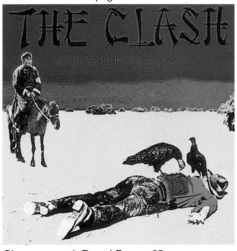

Give em enough Rope LP page 65

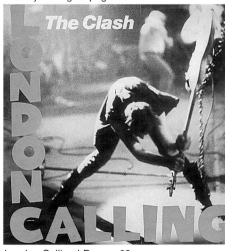

London Calling LP page 69

ash City Rockers page 24

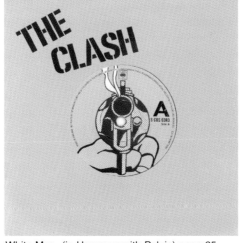

White Man (in Hammersmith Palais) page 25

Tommy Gun page 26

ankrobber page 40

The Call Up page 41

Hitsville UK page 42

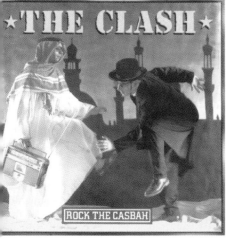

ock the Casbah page 50

Should I Stay or Should I Go/Straight to Hell page 53

This is England page 57

andinista! LP page 74

Combat Rock LP page 81

Cut the Crap LP page 87

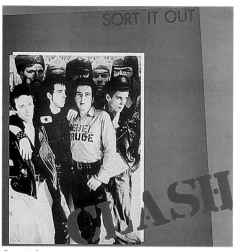

Sort it Out page 102

Clampdown USA page 103

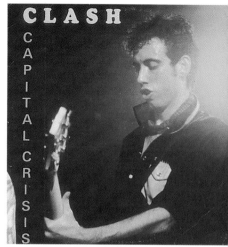

Capital Crisis page 105

16 Tracks page 104

Songbooks page 105

Impossible Mission page 106

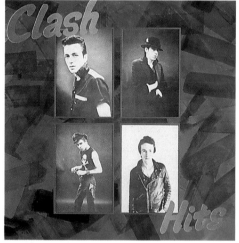

Hits page 107

Combat Rock Outakes page 107

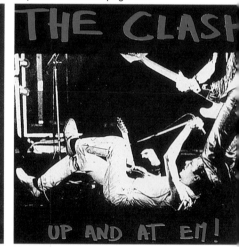

Up and at em! page 107

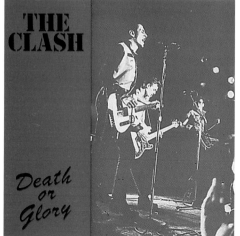

Death or Glory page 108

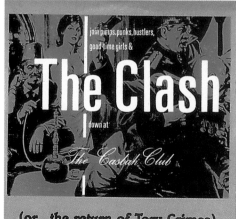

Casbah Club page 109

Live in Paris 84 page 111

The Clash

Track Listing

Side One

Janie Jones
Remote Control
I'm so bored with the USA
White Riot
Hate & War
What's my Name
Deny
London's Burning

Side Two

Career Opportunities
Cheat
Protex Blue
Police & Thieves
48 Hours
Garageland

The Clash's line-up for 'THE CLASH' LP

Mick Jones	Guitar, vocals
Joe Strummer	Guitar, vocals
Paul Simonon	Bass
Tory Crimes (Terry Chimes)	Drums

The Clash

The Clash
UK LP CBS 32232
Release date - 8/4/1977
Sleeve - Orange lettering on black & white picture with green border
Label - Black lettering on orange and yellow background
Produced by - Mickey Foote

The album was recorded over three consecutive Thursday-Sunday weekend sessions, beginning on 10/2/1977 at CBS, Studio 3. Mickey Foote, a friend of Joe's from the 101'er days and Clash Soundman, produced the record. Front cover shot taken outside their rehearsal rooms in Camden Town by Kate Simon. Back shot - a picture of the Notting Hill Riots - was taken by Rocco Macauley, house-mate of Sabastian Conran (Clash's clothes/image man in the early days). It reached No. 12 in the UK Charts.
Production cost £4000.

The Clash, as history will tell us, have been plagued with drummer problems. Tory Crimes (Terry Chimes) did not want to commit himself to the band and in some respects did not fit in with the gang mentality. Hence the classic first album shot shows a strong visual image of 3-man Clash.

The Clash
Argentinean LP 19-749
Release date - 1977
Sleeve - **Front** as UK with added lettering
`London's Burning'
(ARDE Londres);
Back Black lettering on black & white background
Label - Black lettering on orange and yellow background

The Argentinean LP stands out, for its added title of `The Clash ... London's Burning'. The back cover is in black & white and carries the track titles in both English and Spanish, and the label says `Discos CBS' ... nice!

The Clash

The Clash
US LP EPIC JE 36060
Release date - 6/10/1979
Sleeve - As UK except
`The Clash' title moved to
top of sleeve
Label - Silver lettering on blue
background

CBS/EPIC refused to release the Clash's first album in the States complaining it was unsuitable for radio play. The album will sell over 100,000 copies on import to the US, making it the biggest selling import album ever. It finally got repackaged/released in 1979 and made the US Charts at No. 126.

Inner Sleeve
US copy came with this black & white inner sleeve with lyrics.

By the time EPIC decided to release The Clash's first album in the US, the second album had already been released, so they dropped tracks `Deny', `Cheat', `Protex Blue' and `48 Hours' ... and added interim singles `Complete Control', `Clash City Rockers', `Jail Guitar Doors (B- side)', `White Man in Hammersmith Palais' and the track `I fought the Law' from `Cost of Living' EP. Also, initial US copies came with an additional 7" containing two more tracks from `Cost of Living' EP - `Gates of the West' and `Groovy Times'.

**7" Label Groovy Times /
Gates of the West**
Free 7" EPIC AE7 1178
Black lettering on white background
(Free with US album)

Track listing (The Clash USA)

Side One	Side Two
Clash City Rockers	Janie Jones
I'm so bored with the USA	Career Opportunities
Remote Control	What's my Name
Complete Control	Hate & War
White Riot	Police & Thieves
White Man in Hammersmith Palais	Jail Guitar Doors
London's Burning	Garageland
I fought the Law	

The Clash

The Clash
Japanese LP 25-3P-67
Release date - 1977
Sleeve - as UK version with
O/B strip outside
Label - as UK issue

`The Clash' album got a release in Japan at practically the same time as the UK version. This was the first issue in Japan - see below for second issue (which was basically the US version).

The Clash
Japanese LP EPIC 25-3P-139-
140
Release date - 1979
Sleeve - Album sleeve as US
version, but came with extra
overprinted sleeve to promote
Peal Harbour 1979 Tour;
red and yellow
wraparound
Label - Silver lettering on blue
background

Re-promoted in 1979, the US version also got a Japanese release. This version also came with 7" single `Gates of the West / Groovy Times'. The inner sleeve of the Japanese version folded out containing lyrics in English and Japanese.

The Clash
Canadian LP EPIC WJE 36060
Release date - 10/1979
Sleeve - Red lettering on black
& white picture blue border
Label - Silver lettering on blue
background

`The Clash' album was also given a belated Canadian release similar to US with free 7" and same track listing except the background colour of LP was blue instead of green and lettering was red as opposed to orange.

Give 'em Enough Rope

Track Listing

Side One

1) Safe European Home
2) English Civil War
3) Tommy Gun
4) Julie's been Working for the Drug Squad
5) Last Gang in Town

Side Two

6) Guns on the Roof
7) Drug Stabbing Time
8) Stay Free
9) Cheapskates
10) All the Young Punks
(New Boots and Contracts)

The Clash's line-up for 'Give 'em Enough Rope' LP

Mick Jones	Guitar, vocals
Joe Strummer	Guitar, vocals
Paul Simonon	Bass
Topper Headon	Drums

Give 'em Enough Rope

The original February 1978 sessions for `Give 'em Enough Rope' had to be cancelled due to Joe Strummer catching hepatitis; Joe putting this down to the `spitting antics' of the fans at previous Clash gigs. On Joe's recovery, The Clash entered the `Marquee Studios' to cut some demos of tracks Mick and Joe had been working on from a writing trip in Jamaica.

The Clash had initially set their sights on Chris Thomas to produce their follow-up album admiring his work with Roxy Music, but especially on The Sex Pistols' `Never Mind the Bollocks' album. Unfortunately, he was committed to other projects.

With record company pressure and following EPIC's (CBS American label) refusal to release The Clash's debut album, an American radio-friendly producer was sought after. Sandy Pearlman previously known for producing `Blue Oyster Cult' was chosen.

Sessions for the album ran from April to May 1978, beginning at Basing Street Studios (Ladbroke Grove, London), followed on at CBS Studios and Utopia Studios.

A break in the sessions, due to touring commitments, the `Out on Parole' Tour, saw CBS listening to the tapes and stressing the point that they wanted something more polished sound-wise. At one point it is rumoured that the top honcho at CBS, Muff Winwood, even took the tapes himself to the studio to try to remix them.

So Mick & Joe, after the tour, joined Sandy Pearlman at San Francisco's Automatt Studios for more vocal and guitar over-dubs and finally, in September 1978, went on to New York's Record Plant Studios to carry out final remixing. It was a costly exercise running close to £150,000 in all, compared to the first album's £4,000 bill.

`Give 'em Enough Rope' was to be The Clash's first album release in the US.  It was more heavy metal sounding compared to the first album's `Garage' sound, as reviewers at the time pointed out. The lyrics were more Clash story based ... `Guns on the Roof' (Paul & Topper's arrest over pigeon shooting), `Safe European Home' (Mick & Joe's ill-Fated writing trip to Jamaica). `Last Gang in Town' (The Clash possibly??).

The album cover was based on an American postcard called 'End of the Trail' with the Japanese soldier on horseback and Clash Logo superimposed on top.

The Clash fans rushed out to buy their new release pushing it to No. 2 in the UK Charts. Stateside in April 1979, it reached US No. 128.

Give 'em Enough Rope

Give 'em Enough Rope
UK Album CBS 32444
Release date - 10/11/1978
Sleeve - Black lettering over red, blue and yellow tinted sleeve
Label - Black lettering on orange and yellow background
Produced by - Sandy Pearlman

The album cover depicts an East -vs- West showdown with the Chinese army, red flag and Chinese typeface used for group's name against the two vultures feeding off a dead cowboy's corpse. It debuts the UK charts at No. 2.

Poster
Initial copies of the album came with a double-sided poster
Side 1 The Clash Atlas of ... Give 'em Enough Rope. A map of the world showing troubled spots and connecting pictures of terrorist groups, etc.
Side 2 Picture of The Clash in front of map of the world; black & white on red background.

Promotional Album Set UK
`Give 'em Enough Rope' came in a yellow wraparound folder with `Story of The Clash' written inside, with black & white 10" x 8" picture of group and the above poster, all in a clear plastic sleeve with `Clash' stencilled in red on it.

Give 'em Enough Rope

Japanese LP 25-3P-36
Release date - 1978
Sleeve - as UK issue with O/B strip outside
Label - as UK issue

The Clash's second album again got a Japanese release straight away.

Historia de la Musica Rock

Spanish LP LSP 15435
Release date - 1980
Sleeve - Gold, white and black lettering on colour group picture, blue background

This album came out in the 1980s in Spain as a history of rock series. The strange thing about this release is it's not a hits compilation but literally all the tracks from the `Give 'em Enough Rope' album. Also, the front sleeve carries a nice early colour stage shot of the band.

Other Releases

The Clash/
Give 'em Enough Rope

Australian Gatefold 2-LP set
EPIC 241041
Release date - 1980
Australia put the first and second LPs together as a gatefold edition 1980

The Clash/
Give 'em Enough Rope

US LP CBS 82431
Release date - 10/ 11/ 1978

LONDON CALLING

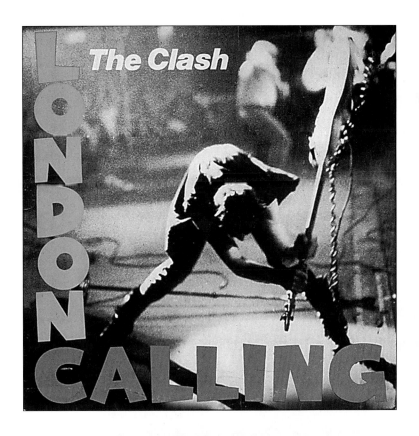

Track Listing

Side One

1) London Calling
2) Brand New Cadillac
3) Jimmy Jazz
4) Hateful
5) Rudie can't Fail

Side Two

6) Spanish Bombs
7) The Right Profile
8) Lost in the Supermarket
9) Clampdown
10) The Guns of Brixton

Side Three

11) Wrong 'em Boyo
12) Death or Glory
13) Koka Kola
14) The Card Cheat

Side Four

15) Lover's Rock
16) Four Horsemen
17) I'm not down
18) Revolution Rock
19) Train in Vain (not track listed)

The Clash's line-up for 'London Calling' LP

Mick Jones — Guitar, vocals
Joe Strummer — Guitar, vocals
Paul Simonon — Bass, vocals
Topper Headon — Drums

London Calling

After the costly and polished exercise that was `Give 'em Enough Rope', The Clash put their minds to recording a more live, fresh sounding album. They took a teac recorder to their newly found rehearsal studios called `Vanilla' in Pimlico, London, and began writing, rehearsing and recording what would eventually be `London Calling', breaking only for group football matches.

The idea of releasing these tapes, as fate would have it, was not to be as their then roadie, Johnny Green, lost the master tapes on London's Underground.

One of Mick Jones' heroes was put forward to produce the new sessions - Guy Stevens who was tracked down in a pub in Oxford Street, cited for his work with Mott The Hoople, one of Mick's favourite bands.

The new sessions would take place in Wessex Studios, North London over a six-week period running from August to September 1979. Rumour has it that the first three days in the studio produced 12 recorded tracks.

Many tales arise from these sessions. Stories of chair throwing by Guy Stevens to get a correct take and Transatlantic phone calls to Mott the Hoople front man, Ian Hunter, for extra vibes; and the story of the cab driver that waited at the studio with his meter running for 12 hours on Guy's insistence, being just some of them.

Annoyed with the price of the `Cost of Living' EP, The Clash wanted to add a 7" to the `London Calling' album. They decided a 12" would be a better idea, and when CBS agreed The Clash let them know that the 12" was in fact a 33rpm 8-track 12", which would make `London Calling' a double album. With their insistence and the loss of some initial royalties, they pushed for the album to be released at a single album price, which was then £5.00.

The Clash, hoping to have one over on their record company, was short-lived when CBS stated that their double album effort would still only count as one album from their record deal.

On release, the album was cited for too many American references even though it was called `London Calling', but was hailed as a classic and many years later was to top a US poll of the Top 100 Albums of All Time.

LONDON CALLING

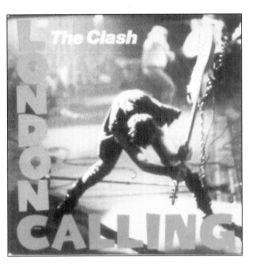

London Calling
UK Album (CBS Clash 3)
Release date - 14/12/1979
Sleeve - **Front** Pink, green and
white lettering on black & white
picture; **Back** Black lettering
on white background with black
& white pictures
Labels - Black lettering on
white background
Produced by - Guy Stevens

Originally titled `The New Testament', name changed to `London Calling'
debuts the UK Charts at No. 9. Mick wrote `Train in Vain' one night when
Kosmo Vinyl (The Clash's one time manager / spokesperson), asked him to
come up with something new for another N.M.E. free disc. It was recorded
and mixed at Wessex Studios the next day. The N.M.E. deal fell through,
so was added just in time to make the LP cut, but not the artwork. So can
be found on Side 4 last track. This little ditty would be The Clash's first US
chart single reaching No. 33.

`London Calling' was dedicated to Henry Bowles a member of the Clash
entourage killed when attacked by a bouncer at a 'Subway Sect' gig.

When released in the US in March 1979, `London Calling' reached No. 27.

The cover picture for `London Calling' was taken by Pennie Smith of Paul
Simonon smashing his bass in frustration at a New York Palladium Show on
21/9/1979.

Inner Sleeves
`London Calling' came with
inner sleeves with lyrics and
pictures ... The Clash's first
album to do so.

LONDON CALLING

Cover Design Original Idea
LP design based on Elvis Presley's first album cover. This LP had same pink and green lettering.

(A)

(B)

(A) London Calling
Japanese LP CBS 35-3P-175-6
Release date - 1979
Sleeve - Gatefold with lyrics on the inside
Label - Black lettering on orange and yellow background

(B) London Calling
Japanese Promotional Package
The above LP came as a promotional package in this folder, plus poster and black & white pictures of group.

Other Releases

Working for the Clampdown / Brand New Cadillac / Spanish Bombs
US 10" Promo only EPIC 788
Sleeve - White die-cut sleeve

Clampdown / Lost in the Supermarket / The Card Cheat / London Calling
US Four-Track sampler
Promo EPIC XSM 166872
Sleeve - Black plain die-cut sleeve, promo stamped
Label - Black lettering on white background

London Calling
U.S. LP EPIC 36328
Release date:- 1/ 1980

BLaCk MaRket CLaSh

Black Market Clash
US 10" LP EPIC TAL 36846
Release date - 10/1980
Sleeve - **Front** Blue and brown lettering on brown tinted picture;
Back Brown lettering on white background
Label - Black lettering on blue and yellow background

The classic cover shot is a picture by Rocco Redondo, taken at the 1976 Notting Hill Carnival ... a police confrontation on Portobello Road.

Label design
Not the usual EPIC label, this release was on EPIC's `NU disk' imprint.

The Clash's US record label, EPIC, had seen the demand for import material and were keen to exploit it. So they put together this 10" package containing unavailable tracks in the US. The original version of `Capital Radio' from N.M.E. EP B-sides `Pressure Drop', `City of the Dead', `The Prisoner', `Armagideon Time', and its two dub versions, `Justice Tonight/Kick it Over'; UK A-side `Bankrobber', `Rubber-Dub', `Cheat' which was dropped from the US version of The Clash's first album, and last but not least a 1978 demo of Booker T and the M.G.'s `Time is Tight' remixed by Bill Price.

Track Listing

Side One

1) Capital Radio One
2) The Prisoner
3) Pressure Drop
4) Cheat
5) City of the Dead
6) Time is Tight

Side Two

7) Bank Robber/ Robber Dub
8) Armagideon Time
9) Justice Tonight/ Kick It Over

Other Releases

Black Market Clash
Canadian 12" LP EPIC 12 EXP 340
Sleeve - as US version but 12" size

Black Market Clash
New Zealand 12" LP EPIC EX 12006
Sleeve - 10" US sleeve with 2" white border

Black Market Clash
Australian 12" LP EPIC EX 12006
Sleeve - 10" US sleeve with 2" white border

Black Market Clash
Spanish 12" LP CBS S 84735
Sleeve - as US but 12" size

Sandinista!

Track Listing

Side One
1) The Magnificent Seven
2) Hitsville UK
3) Junco Partner
4) Ivan meets G.I. Joe
5) The Leader
6) Something about England

Side Two
7) Rebel Waltz
8) Look Here
9) The Crooked Beat
10) Somebody got Murdered
11) One more Time
12) One more Time Dub

Side Three
13) Lightning Strikes
    (not once but twice)
14) Up in Heaven
    (not only here)
15) Corner Soul
16) Let's Go Crazy
17) If Music could talk
18) The Sound of the Sinners

Side Four
19) Police on my Back
20) Midnight Log
21) The Equaliser
22) The Call Up
23) Washington Bullets

Side Five
24) Lose this skin
25) Charlie don't Surf
26) Mensforth Hill
27) Junkie Slip
28) Kingston Advice
29) The Street Parade

Side Six
30) Version City
31) Living in Fame
32) Silicone on Sapphire
33) Version Pardner
34) Career Opportunities
35) Shepherd's Delight

Sandinista! LP Line up

Mick Jones	Guitar, vocals
Joe Strummer	Guitar, vocals
Paul Simonon	Bass, vocals
Topper Headon	Drums

Sandinista!

After touring the `London Calling' album in the US in 1979, The Clash decided to stay on in New York. Paul Simonon had been offered a part in a film called `All Washed Up' and had headed off to Canada for six weeks' shooting.

The rest of the group booked some studio time in New York's Power Station Studios to demo some possible future singles. After recording a version of `The Equals', `Police on my Back', the studio became fully booked. They were offered a block booking of three weeks at Electric Ladyland Studios and decided to take it. With Paul missing from the ranks, they called over Mickey Gallagher (keyboards) and Norman Watt-Roy (bass) from Ian Dury and The Blockheads to take part in the sessions.

With Norman Watt-Roy, they cut `Magnificent Seven' and a couple of other tracks, and on his departure Topper, Mick and Joe took turns laying down bass parts, with Mickey Dread (producer) at the controls. They began to build up a batch of songs.

On Paul Simonon's return, they decided to fly to Kingston's Channel One Studios in Jamaica to cut some extra tracks, `Junco Partner, a cover version song Joe used to play with the 101'ers, and `Kingston Advice'.

The next turn of events, the refusal by CBS to release the `Bankrobber' single at the time, riled the band so much that they threatened to down tools and bate CBS by telling them they had another double album they wanted to release.

On returning to the UK, they booked themselves into Wessex Studios as they had with `London Calling' and began putting the album together. As recording progressed, they soon had 30 tracks to choose from.

With so many tracks recorded, they could see that a double album would simply not accommodate that amount of material. So they approached CBS with a deal - to waiver their royalty payments on the first 200,000 copies of the LP if it could be a triple album and sell at the fixed price of a double album, £5.99. A brave move since up to this time `London Calling' in total had sold 180,000 copies.

One thinks the record company were happy with this deal. As time would tell us, the album in question would go on to sell in excess of 800,000 copies, of which over half would be sold in the US at a full price tag of US$14.95.

On the `16 Tons' Tour of 1979, just prior to these recordings, the group met a radical named Armstrong who told the group of the victory in Nicaragua of left-wing Sandinista rebels over military dictator General Somoza. On recording the `Washington Bullets' track, Joe can be heard at the end of the track shouting `Sandinista'.

When the group had finished the album, a suitable name was looked for to call it. They opted to educate the world a little and give the space a `Clash' album title would be afforded around the world to a cause, and hopefully at least get people talking and asking questions about its title.

They called the album

Sandinista!

Sandinista!
UK Album CBS FSLN 1
Release date - 12/12/1980
Sleeve - **Front** Red lettering
on black & white background;
Back Black lettering on red
background
Label:- White lettering on black
background with red / black
number's for each side
Produced by - The Clash
Version mixes by - Mickey
Dread

`Sandinista' got a Xmas release date.  It was a triple album selling at the price of a double LP.  It reached No. 19 in the UK Charts. Cover shot was another `Pennie Smith' shot taken against a wall at Kings Cross Station, London. Cat. No. FSLN stands for `Fronte Sandinista Liberacion Nacional'.

(A) Fold-out Lyric Sheet
The album came with a fold-out
lyric sheet designed and illus-
trated by political cartoonist
Steve Bell under the title `The
Armagideon Times No. 3'.

**(B) UK Press Kit for
Sandinista**
Containing press cuttings, gig
reviews and two black & white
group pictures.

(A) Fold-out Lyric Sheet

(B) UK Press Kit

**Armagideon Times
Magazines**
Issue one, issue two
Issue one was 1980 `Sixteen
Tons' Tour Programme

`Armagideon Times' were The Clash's info mags containing pictures of the group, lyrics, drawings, etc. you could send off for. There were only two issues, the third being a lyric sheet as stated above.

Sandinista!

Sandinista! Track Notes ...

As Sandinista was heavily influenced by Reggae/Dub, some of the extra tracks were versions of other tracks as listed below ...

New Version	Reworking of
Version Partner	Junco Partner
Silicone on Sapphire	Washington Bullets
If Music could Talk	Shepherds Delight
Mensforth Hill	Something about England

Other Notes

Topper wrote and sings...`Ivan Meets G.I. Joe'
Paul wrote and sings...`The Crooked Beat'
Tymon Dogg wrote and sings...`Lose this Skin'
Mickey Gallagher's kids sing Karaoke version...............`Career Opportunities'
Mick Jones & Ellen Foley Duet.......................................`Hitsville UK'
Commissioned by Jack Nitzche for Al Pacino's
1980 movie `Cruising'...................................................`Somebody got Murdered'

Sandinista Sampler

Canadian Sampler
CBS CDN 34
Promo release date - 1980
Sleeve - Plain white die-cut sleeve
Label - Black lettering on grey and blue background

To promote Sandinista 3-LP set, a single LP of highlights was put together and sent to DJs, etc. The US also put out a sampler single LP.See next page.

Track Listing

Side One

1) Hitsville UK
2) Ivan meets G.I. Joe
3) Somebody got Murdered
4) The Call Up
5) Police on my Back
6) The Magnificent Seven

Side Two

7) Lightning Strikes (Not once but twice)
8) The Equaliser
9) Version City
10) Up in Heaven (Not only here)
11) One More Time
12) Junco Partner

Sandinista!

Sandinista Sampler

US Sampler XSM 168445
Promo release date - 1980
Sleeve - Plain white promo
stamped
Label - Black lettering on white
background

Track Listing

Side One

1) Police on my Back
2) Somebody got Murdered
3) The Call Up
4) Washington Bullets
5) Ivan meets G.I. Joe
6) Hitsville UK

Side Two

7) Up in Heaven (Not only here)
8) The Magnificent Seven
9) The Leader
10) Junco Partner
11) One More Time
12) The Sound of Sinners

The US version has different track listing to the Canadian single Promo LP.

Other Sandinista Related Releases

Police on my Back / The Crooked Beat

Australian Promo only 7" ES
604
No picture sleeve
Sandinista!

Sandinista!

U.S. LP EPIC 37037
Releasa Date:- 1/ 1981

On its US March release, it
climbed to No. 24 in the US
Charts.

New Rock (Magazine) Australian flexi (4 Groups)

Clash:- Lightning Strikes
Adam & the Ants:- Antmusic
Police:- De Do Do Do De Da Da Da
Cheap Trick:- Stop the Game

If Music Could Talk

If Music Could Talk
US Promotional LP EPIC
XSM 168562
Release date - Promotional only 1981
Sleeve - White lettering on grey background, black & white picture
Label - Black lettering on white background

Promotional only US release. Distributed to radio stations in America to tie in with the release of `Sandinista' album. Interviews with Mick, Joe, Topper and Paul interspersed with tracks from the album.

Track Listing

Side One

Interview with Paul Simonon
In between tracks:
Junco Partner
One More Time

Interview with Mick Jones
In between tracks:
Hitsville UK
The Magnificent Seven

Side Two

Interview with Joe Strummer
In between tracks:
Washington Bullets
Call Up
Police on my Back

Interview with Topper Headon
In between tracks:
Ivan meets G.I. Joe
Somebody got Murdered

ELLEN FOLEY - SPIRIT OF ST LOUIS

Ellen Foley
Spirit of St Louis
UK LP EPIC S EPC 84809
Release Date - 3/1981
Sleeve - Purple lettering on
white background with black &
white picture
Label - Black lettering on blue
background
Produced by Mick Jones

Mick Jones' then girlfriend Ellen Foley, formerly Meatloaf's backing singer, was also signed to CBS / EPIC. When it came to record her second solo album, Mick took the producer's chair. This is an important Clash related project as it was one of very few times the Strummer / Jones writing partnership would work together outside The Clash perimeters. They wrote six of the twelve songs together, including the first single from the album `The Shuttered Palace'. The album also features Topper on drums, Paul Simonon on bass, along with Norman Watt-Roy (Blockheads) and Joe Strummer on guitar. Mick also features on guitar/ vocals.

Track Listing

1) The Shuttered Palace (Strummer/ Jones)
2) Torchlight (Strummer/ Jones)
3) Beautiful Waste of Time (Tymon Dogg)
4) The Death of the Psychoanalyst of Salvador Dali (Strummer/ Jones)
5) M.P.H. (Strummer/ Jones)
6) My Legionnaire (Asso/ Monnot/ mair)

7) Theatre of Cruelty (Strummer/ Jones)
8) How Glad I am (Williams/ Harrison)
9) Phases of Travel (Foley)
10) Game of a Man (Tymon Dogg)
11) Indestructible (Tymon Dogg)
12) In the Killing Hour (Strummer/ Jones)

7" Single Releases from LP

The Shuttered Palace /
Beautiful Waste of Time
UK 7" EPIC 9522
Release date - 2/1981

Torchlight /
Game of a Man
UK 7" EPIC A 1160
Release date - 4/1981

Combat Rock ... Rat Patrol from Fort Bragg

Track Listing

Side One

1) Know your Rights
2) Car Jamming
3) Should I Stay or Should I Go
4) Rock the Casbah
5) Red Angel Dragnet
6) Straight to Hell

Side Two

7) Overpowered by Funk
8) Atom Tan
9) Sean Flynn
10) Ghetto Defendant
11) Inoculated City
12) Death is a Star

The Clash's line-up for 'Combat Rock' LP

Mick Jones	Guitar, vocals
Joe Strummer	Guitar, vocals
Paul Simonon	Bass
Topper Headon	Drums

Combat ROCk ... Rat Patrol....FrOm FOrt Bragg

Under the working title of `Rat Patrol from Fort Bragg' work was commencing on the follow-up album to `Sandinista!'. Demos were being recorded using a mobile sound van at EAR Studios, off Latimer Road, London.

However, Mick Jones was far from pleased with the situation and preferred the working surroundings of New York. With the ultimatum of "If you do it in New York, I'll turn up", the sessions were transferred to New York's Electric Ladyland Studios. Mick Jones took over the reins for the project and with his dance influences intact the tracks were spiralling to be long raga-length tracks.

It seemed The Clash could be again looking at a double album length release. When Mick's finished mixes of 15 tracks were presented to the rest of the band just as they were about to leave for a Far East tour, they all rejected it citing over-indulgence and over-length.

Joe wanted a direct single album that the band could tour / promote and make money for themselves, as the band was just out of debt to CBS for the first time in their careers.

With tensions already strained between Joe and Mick, Joe pushed forward with his single album plan and on Bernie Rhode's suggestion, Glyn Johns, who had worked with The Beatles, Rolling Stones and The Faces, was brought in to oversee the production.

Glyn's job was to cut the album down to size, so some leftfield material like `The Beautiful People' and `Kill Time' were taken out completely and are still un-released today (see Bootleg Bible - Combat Rock Demos LP), while other tracks were edited and remixed to suit.

Even the title was edited down to `Combat Rock'. The Clash got a single album that turned out to be their biggest selling album. Hopefully one day with the advent of CD, a limited release of Mick Jones version could see the light of day ...
who knows??

COmbat ROCk

Combat Rock
UK LP CBS FMLN2
Release date - 14/5/1982
Sleeve - **Front** Red lettering
on colour picture, silver border;
Back Yellow, red and white
lettering on silver/grey
(camouflage) background
Label - Yellow, white and red
lettering on yellow and black
(camouflage) background
Produced by - Glyn Jones

Front sleeve shot was taken in Thailand by Pennie Smith. The Cat. No. FMLN stands for 'Farabundo Marti Liberacicn Nacional', El Salvador's rebel forces. `Combat Rock' hit the UK Charts at No. 2 and remained in there for 23 weeks. On it's release in America in January 1983, it hit No. 7 and sold over a million copies.

 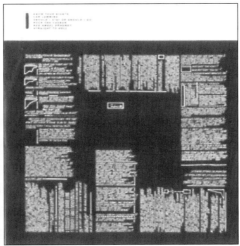

(A) Poster
Initial copies of `Combat Rock'
came with this poster. Again,
shot in Thailand by Pennie
Smith and tinted by Paul
Simonon. **(LEFT)**

(B) Inner Sleeve
Inner Sleeve with lyrics was
designed by Futura 2000, who
also contributed backing vocals
to the album. **(RIGHT)**

Combat Rock
Japanese LP EPIC 25-3P-353
Release date - 1982
Sleeve - as UK with O/B band
Label - as UK

`Combat Rock' got a Japanese release simultaneously with the UK.

Combat Rock

Combat Rock
USA LP EPIC FE 37689
Release date - 5/1982
Sleeve - as UK

The US release of the album was delayed slightly due to insistence from The Clash that EPIC remove the `Home taping is killing music' statement written on back sleeve.

Combat Rock
USA Picture Disc
EPIC AS 99-1592
Release date - Promotional only, not for sale
Picture label - **Front** White and red lettering on yellow / black square, with camouflage background.
Sticker on plastic sleeve, red and white lettering with track details, etc.;
Back Red lettering on black & white picture of group.

EPIC decided to promote `Combat Rock' LP in the US by having a promotional picture disc made. However, as shown, there were two editions of this picture disc.

(B)

Combat Rock
USA Picture Disc EPIC
AL 37689
Release date - Promotional only, not for sale
Picture label - Camouflage (green, yellow, brown) picture disc with EPIC label, silver lettering on blue background, sticker on plastic sleeve - as above

(B) Insert Sticker
Red lettering `Face the Future' on black & white picture of group. Both editions came with this sticker.

By the time the second single, `Rock the Casbah' was released, being heavily rotated on MTV, and with the added eight concerts as support to 'The Who' playing to 50,000-80,000 people a night. The album raced up to No. 7 in US Charts and sold over one million copies.

The WORLd ACCOrding tO
The ClaSh

The World According to The Clash
US Promotional LP EPIC
XSM 170729
Release date - Promotional only, 1982
Sleeve - White lettering on black background
Label - Silver lettering on black and blue background

Distributed in 1982 to tie in with the release of `Combat Rock' album. This compilation consists of highlights from the American released albums to date, put together for radio and in-store play purposes.

Track Listing

Side One

1) Rock the Casbah
2) Clampdown
3) Train in Vain
4) Brand New Cadillac
5) Magnificent Dance

Side Two

6) This is Radio Clash
7) I fought the Law
8) Police on my Back
9) London Calling
11) Lost in the Supermarket
12) Should I Stay or Should I Go

Super Black Market Clash

Super Black Market Clash

UK Triple 10" LP
Columbia 4745461
Release date - 1993
Sleeve - **Front** Red and black lettering on blue and yellow tinted sleeve;
Back Black lettering on yellow, brown and red background
Label - Black lettering on red background

`Super Black Market Clash' came with excellent liner notes of dates, track recording details etc.With the additional tracks and all of `Black Market Clash' present resulting in a triple 10" release.

Inner Sleeves

Nice tinted inner sleeves
Front Group picture, red, blue and yellow tints
Back sides White lettering on black background; 1st 10" red surround, 2nd 10" blue surround, 3rd 10" yellow surround

When Columbia (Sony) thought to re-issue `Black Market Clash' in 1993, they decided to update the package and add extra tracks, so Kosmo Vinyl (Clash's spokesman) was brought in to compile it. In addition to all the tracks on `Black Market Clash', one now got extra B - sides of singles (Sides Two & Five), the whole of `The Cost of Living' EP (Side Three), all the tracks that did not make the US release of The Clash's first album (Side One), and some extended versions of songs `Magnificent Dance', `Mustapha Dance' and `Cool Out', which is a superior US remix of `Call Up'.

Track Listing

Side One
1) 1977
2) Protex Blue
3) Deny
4) Cheat
5) 48 Hours
6) Listen

Side Two
1) Jail Guitar Doors
2) The City of the Dead
3) The Prisoner
4) Pressure Drop
5) 1-2 Crush on You

Side Three
1) Groovy Times
2) Gates of the West
3) Capital Radio Two
4) Time is Tight

Side Four
1) Justice Tonight/Kick it Over
2) Robber Dub

Side Five
1) Stop the World
2) The Cool Out
3) First Night Back in London
4) Long Time Jerk
5) Cool Confusion

Side Six
1) The Magnificent Dance
2) This is Radio Clash
3) Mustapha Dance

Cut the Crap

Track Listing

Side One

Dictator
Dirty Punk
We are the Clash
Are you red...y
Cool under Heat
Movers and Shakers

Side Two

This is England
Three Card Trick
Play to Win
Fingerpoppin'
North and South
Life is Wild

The Clash's line-up for 'Cut the Crap' LP

Joe Strummer	Vocals / Guitar
Paul Simonon	Bass
Nick Sheppard	Guitar / Vocals
Vince White	Guitar / Vocals
Pete Howard	Drums

Cut the Crap....Cut to the Story

With Bernie Rhodes back in the manager's seat, and with the sacking of Mick Jones, The Clash were going through a new `back to basics' era.

A new line-up was put together through auditions held at The Electric Ballroom, Camden Town, where guitarists had to play along to three backing tracks. The idea would be that no-one would know it was The Clash they were auditioning for.

They already had a new drummer in Pete Howard, a replacement for Topper Headon who was sacked in late 1982 (see Brief History).

After 300 auditions, they now had two new guitarists, as Joe wanted to concentrate on singing duties. The new Clash line-up was:

Joe Strummer	Vocals / Guitar
Paul Simonon	Bass
Nick Sheppard	Guitar / Vocals (ex Cortinas)
Vince White	Guitar / Vocals
Pete Howard	Drums

After an energetic start, a US tour, some European festival dates and a `busking' tour around North England, Joe seemed to get disillusioned with the way things were going. With some personal problems to sort out, Joe distanced himself from the project.

Bernie Rhodes began taking control over the `Cut the Crap' album. With the help of studio engineers and some synthesizers, Bernie set about making what he thought a Clash album should sound like in 1985. Working up Joe's songs in some cases, demos, and under the pseudonym of `Jose Unidos' (a nod to Mick Jones' early production disguise of `Pepe Unidos'), Bernie produced the `Cut the Crap' album in Munich and credited the songs to Strummer / Rhodes.

The bad feelings were so apparent that by the time `Cut the Crap' hit the streets the band were no more. The hired hands of Nick, Vince and Pete had left the band, and Joe and Paul called it a day, perhaps hoping Mick Jones would return to the fold which, as history tells us, was not the case ...

Cut the Crap

Cut the Crap
UK LP CBS 26601
Release date - 11/1985
Sleeve - Silver lettering on silver yellow background
Label - **Side One** Black lettering on red background; **Side Two** Black lettering on yellow background
Produced by - Jose Unidos (Bernie Rhodes)

Title taken from George Miller's `Mad Max 2' film; Max, the film's hero, shouts in the final scenes of the movie, "Cut the crap, I'm the only real chance you've got". The album will climb the UK Charts to No. 16 and, in 1986, the US Charts to No. 88.

Inner sleeve
One side featuring lyrics of dictator, movers & shakers, three card trick.
Otherside:- B/W Group picture around Paul's place.

Fingerpoppin'
Promo only 12" USA EAS 2277

**Are you Red...y /
Three Card Trick**
Promo only 12" USA

Both the above promo releases helped push the album in the States.

**Are you Red...y /
Three Card Trick**
Australian promo only EPIC ES 1113

The Story Of The Clash, Volume 1

Track Listing

Side A

1) The Magnificent Seven
2) Rock the Casbah
3) This is Radio Clash
4) Should I Stay or Should I Go
5) Straight to Hell
6) Armagideon Time

Side C

14) White Man in Hammersmith Palais
15) London's Burning
16) Janie Jones
17) Tommy Gun
18) Complete Control
19) Capital Radio
20) White Riot
21) Career Opportunities

Side B

7) Clampdown
8) Train in Vain
9) Guns of Brixton
10) I fought the Law
11) Somebody got Murdered
12) Lost in the Supermarket
13) Bankrobber

Side D

22) Clash City Rockers
23) Safe European Home
24) Stay Free
25) London Calling
26) Spanish Bombs
27) English Civil War
28) Police and Thieves

The Story Of The Clash, Volume 1

The Story of The Clash, Volume 1
UK Double LP CBS 4602441
Release date - 21/3/1988
Sleeve - Gold lettering on red tinted picture of band
Label - White lettering on red background, each side has head shot of one Clash member -
 Joe, Mick, Paul and Topper

Released in 1988, this 'best of' Contains some singles and some album tracks. It climbed the UK Charts to No. 1 and remained in the Charts for ten weeks.

Inner Sleeves
Each side contains a picture of one member as shown.
The writing on the inner sleeves is by Albert Transom (Joe Strummer) and is a brief synopsis of band's career/high-lights through the eyes of Joe...

Contains a strong track listing that runs in no particular order ... Volume 2 ... time will tell ...

Crucial Music, The Clash
A Collection Of Rare Tracks & B-Sides

A Collection of Rare Tracks & B-sides

US CD CBS Relativity A21432
Release date - 1990
CD sleeve - Red and blue writing on black & white Clash newspaper write-up;
Insert Colour group shot
CD label - Red and black lettering on silver lettering background

A 1990 CD US only release of then hard-to-find tracks, made up of the songs left off US version of The Clash's first LP - `Cheat', `Protex Blue', `48 Hours' and `Deny', UK B-sides - `1977', `London's Burning', `1-2 Crush on You', `Stop the World' and two cuts from `Cost of Living' EP - `Groovy Times' and `Gates of the West'.  Now made redundant by `Clash on Broadway' and other later releases. But at close of press the only place you can find 'London's Burning' (live) on CD.

Track Listing

1) 1977
2) London's Burning (live)
3) Deny
4) Cheat
5) 48 Hours
6) Protex Blue
7) Groovy Times
8) Gates of the West
9) 1-2 Crush on You
10) Stop the World

The Singles

The Clash, The Singles
UK CD Columbia 4689462
Release date -11/1991
CD sleeve - Red, yellow and white lettering on blue and black background; folds out to contain lyrics ot all singles one side, other side blue and black collage of Clash pictures
CD label - Black lettering on silver background

This CD only release was put out on the strength of the re-release hit of `Should I Stay or Should I Go' and is what it says ... The Singles `White Riot' to `Should I Stay or Should I Go' inclusive.
It peaks at No 68 in the UK charts.

Nice to have the lyrics, nice Pennie Smith pictures, shame no vinyl copy ...
I suppose it's not a boardroom concern any more ... shame.

Track Listing

1) White Riot
2) Remote Control
3) Complete Control
4) Clash City Rockers
5) White Man in Hammersmith Palais
6) Tommy Gun
7) English Civil War
8) I Fought the Law
9) London Calling

10) Train in Vain
11) Bankrobber
12) The Call Up
13) Hitsville UK
14) Magnificent Seven
15) This is Radio Clash
16) Know your Rights
17) Rock the Casbah
18) Should I Stay or Should I Go

TWeLVe INCh MiXeS

The Clash,
Twelve Inch Mixes
Greek Mini LP Columbia
COL 4501231
Release date - 1992
Sleeve - White and yellow
 lettering on grey and black
picture with yellow border
Label - Black lettering on red
background

Columbia issued a five-track mid-priced CD called `Twelve Inch Mixes'.
We being vinyl fetishes, tracked down the Greek vinyl version which
tends to happen especially in the vinyl/CD crossover period. The main
label would sometimes not bother with a vinyl version of a release, but
one could be found in a more vinyl-friendly territory, ie. Greece. This
release compiled The Clash's most famous extended versions and
even includes the later `This is England'.

Track Listing

1) London Calling
2) The Magnificent Dance
3) This is Radio Clash
4) Rock the Casbah
5) This is England

Clash on Broadway

Clash on Broadway
3-CD Box Set EPIC/ Legacy
46991
Release date:-1991
Box - White lettering on black &
white box
Contains - 3 CDs, 66 page
booklet and CD size lyric
booklet

The ultimate Clash compilation to date. Sixty-four tracks in total (Track No. 64
being a non- listed `Street Parade' on the end of CD 3). The CDs feature two
Guy Stevens Polydor demos recorded in November 1976 - `Janie Jones' and
`Career Opportunities', three previously unreleased tracks -  `One Emotion',
`Every Little Bit Hurts' and `Midnight to Stevens'. The rest being various B-sides,
album tracks, some live versions, singles, etc. One can see the band's taste
through this collectic track listing, ie. no `Remote Control' and nothing from
`Cut the Crap', which is even left off the basic discography.

The 66-page booklet contains pictures, mainly Pennie Smith's and Bob Gruen's,
extracts from Lester Bang's 1977 NME `Clash' feature, and a specially
commissioned essay on The Clash by Patti Smith's guitarist, Lenny Kaye,
 followed by a track breakdown interspersed with stories / comments by band
members, roadies, etc.

This CD set never got a vinyl release ... shame. It's made various other Clash
compilations redundant. Nice packaging, which goes to show you need a band
insider, in this case Kosmo Vinyl, to turn a record company buck-making
exercise into something worth buying...

Other related releases

Clash on Broadway
14 track sampler US EPIC ESK4274
Promo release:- 1991

The Clash Mega Mix
US Promo 12" CLA-25
Promo release:- 1991

Clash on Broadway The Interviews
US Promo CD ESK 4337
Promo release 1991

Clash on Broadway

Track Listing

CD 1

1) Janie Jones (demo)
2) Career Opportunities (demo)
3) White Riot
4) 1977
5) I'm so Bored with the USA
6) Hate and War
7) What's my Name
8) Deny
9) London's Burning
10) Protex Blue
11) Police and Thieves
12) 48 Hours
13) Cheat
14) Garageland
15) Capital Radio One
16) Complete Control
17) Clash City Rockers
18) City of the Dead
19) Jail Guitar Doors
20) The Prisoner
21) White Man in Hammersmith Palais
22) Pressure Drop
23) 1-2 Crush on You
24) English Civil War (live)
25) I Fought the Law (live)

CD 2

1) Safe European Home
2) Tommy Gun
3) Julie's been Working for the Drug Squad
4) Stay Free
5) One Emotion
6) Groovy Times
7) Gates of the West
8) Armagideon Time
9) London Calling
10) Brand New Cadillac
11) Rude can't Fail
12) The Guns of Brixton
13) Spanish Bombs
14) Lost in the Supermarket
15) The Right Profile
16) The Card Cheat
17) Death or Glory
18) Clampdown
19) Train in Vain
20) Bankrobber

CD 3

1) Police on my Back
2) The Magnificent Seven
3) The Leader
4) The Call Up
5) Somebody got Murdered
6) Washington Bullets
7) Broadway
8) Lightning Strikes (Not Once but Twice) (live)
9) Every Little Bit Hurts
10) Stop the World
11) Midnight to Stevens
12) This is Radio Clash
13) Cool Confusion
14) Red Angel Dragnet
15) Ghetto Defendant
16) Rock the Casbah
17) Should I Stay or Should I Go (US single version)
18) Straight to Hell (unedited)
19) Street Parade (not listed)

Studio Demos
Side One Oh Baby Oh / One Emotion/ Mona
Side Two You Can't Judge a Book by Looking at the Cover/Kill Time/The Beautiful People
Sleeve - Purple lettering on purple and black background

Studio outtakes - `Oh Baby Oh' was later reworked
into `Gates of the West', rest un-released. `You Can't Judge' is a cover version and
`Kill Time/The Beautiful People' combat rock outtakes. European Bootleg

Studio Outtakes
Side One 1-2 Crush on You/ City of the Dead
Side Two Pressure Drop
Sleeve - Yellow and black cover, green vinyl,

B-sides non album tracks. European Bootleg

Give 'em Enough Rope Demos
(Psychedelic Moose Records PMR 005)
Side One Drug Stabbing Time/ Safe European Home
Side Two Julie's been Working for the Drug Squad/ Stay Free
Sleeve - Black & white wraparound cover

Studio outtakes from second Clash album `Give 'em Enough Rope'.
European Bootleg.

Live in NYC 1979 (SFR 006)
Side One London Calling
Side Two English Civil War
Sleeve - Yellow and black wraparound sleeve

Live from New York Palladium 21st September 1979.
US Bootleg.

Virgin Hormones EP (VH-001)
The Clash...... Coke adds Life
Magazine....... I Love You, Ya Dummy
Gang of 4...... Damage Goods
Buzzcocks..... Love you More
Sleeve - Black & white slick

4-group compilation The Clash Track Live (NY Palladium 1979).
US Bootleg.

Clash Bootleg Bible

Three singles by new Clash line-up

`R&B Showdown' Big City Volume 1 (FC 002)
Side One Ready for War?/Complete Control
Side Two In the Pouring Rain/ Clampdown
Sleeve - Blue / black & white cover

Live in Paramount Theatre, Seattle, Washington, 30 May 1984 mixing desk.
European Bootleg, 500 copies only.

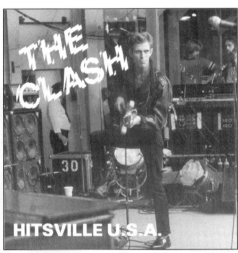

`Hitsville USA' Big City Volume 2 (CCR 002)
Side One Sex Mad Roar/ Janie Jones
Side Two Straight to Hell/ Brand New Cadillac
Sleeve - Black & white cover

Live in University or Oregon, Eugene, 29/5/1984 mixing desk.
European Bootleg, 500 copies only.

`Chicago Shakedown' Big City Volume 3 (CCR 003)
Side One Clash City Rockers/ Three Card Trick
Side Two Safe European Home/ White Riot
Sleeve - Black & white cover

Live in Aragon Ballroom Chicago, 17/5/1984 mixing desk.
European Bootleg, 500 copies only.

Take It or Leave It (Wise/P.F.P.)
Side One London's Burning/ 1977/
I'm so Bored with the USA/ Pressure Drop/
Hate and War/ 48 Hours/ Deny / Capital Radio/
Police and Thieves
Side Two Cheat/ Remote Control/
Career Opportunities / Janie Jones/ White Riot/
Garageland/ 1977
Sleeve - Deluxe black & white cover

Live at The Electric Circus, Manchester, 8 May 1977.
European Bootleg.

White Riot Live (P.F.P.)
Side One London's Burning/ 1977/
I'm so Bored with the USA/ Pressure Drop/
Hate and War/ 48 Hours/ Deny / Capital Radio/
Police and Thieves
Side Two Cheat / Remote Control/
Career Opportunities / Janie Jones / White Riot /
Garageland/ 1977
Sleeve - White sleeve rubber stamped

Live Electric Circus Manchester 8 May 1977.
European Bootleg.
Same as above but Different sleeve.

Cardiff -77 (CF 10080)
Side One I'm so Bored with the USA/ Hate and War/
48 Hours/ Deny/ Police and Thieves.
Side Two Cheat/ Capital Radio/ What's my Name/
Protex Blue/ Remote Control/ Garageland/ 1977
Sleeve - White cover, rubber stamp

Says Cardiff 77 but in fact its Leicester De Montfort Hall 2 July 1977.
European Bootleg.

The Clash Bootleg Bible

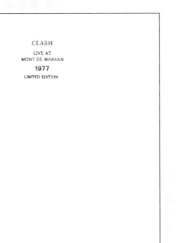

Mont de Marsan 1977 (CC677)
Side One London's Burning/ Capital Radio/ Complete Control/ Pressure Drop / The Prisoner/ I'm so Bored with the USA/ Cheat / Hate and War/ Clash City Rockers
Side Two Remote Control/ Career Opportunities / Janie Jones / White Riot / Garageland / 1977/ What's my Name/ Complete Control/ Protex Blue/ London's Burning
Sleeve - White sleeve, embossed lettering

Live in France, 5 August 1977. Red vinyl, only 650 made. Swedish Bootleg.

Red China (Fashion Mall Productions)
Side One Career Opportunities / White Riot / Janie Jones / London's Burning / 1977/ Listen
Side Two 1-2 Crush on You/ Pressure Drop/ The Prisoner/ Capital Radio/ Interview
Sleeve - Red and black Deluxe sleeve

Side One - Tracks 1-6, Polydor demos, November 1976; Track 6, Capital Radio EP
Side Two - Tracks 1-3, B-sides; Tracks 4-5, Capital Radio EP
European Bootleg.

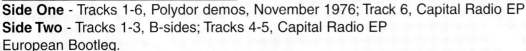

Another History of The Clash Volume 1
Side A Career Opportunities/ White Riot/ JanieJones/ London's Burning/1977/ Pressure Drop / The Prisoner
Side B Safe European Home / Julie's been Working for the Drug Squad / Stay Free/ Groovy Times/ Drug Stabbing Time/ Last Gang in Town
Side C It's not Over/ One Emotion/ Clash City Rockers / Tommy Gun/ I'm so Bored with the USA/ London's Burning/ White Riot
Side D Career Opportunities / 1977/ Janie Jones (instrumental)/ Heartbreak Hotel/ Straight to Hell / Rock the Casbah/ Should I Stay or Should I Go
Sleeve - black & white cover

Side A - Polydor demos,11/ 1976 (not 77 as stated) Side B + first 3 tracks, Side C - Give 'em Enough Rope demos, 3 / 1978 Last 3 tracks, Side C + first 4 tracks, Side D - Mickey Foote demos, Beaconsfield Jan 77 not 76 as stated on LP. Last 3 tracks, Side D - Combat Rock demos, 1982. Japanese Bootleg.

Clash on Tour
(instant lettering)
Side One London's Burning/ Complete Control/
1977/White Man/ Capital Radio/
City of the Dead/ The Prisoner/ White Riot /
Paris's Singing (London's Burning)
Side Two Tommy Gun/ I Fought the Law /
Jail Guitar Doors/ Clash City Rockers / Drug Squad /
Protex Blue/ Guns on the Roof / Stay Free /
Police and Thieves/ Blitzkrieg Bop / Janie Jones /
English Civil War
Sleeve - Deluxe black & white cover

Live in Paris, 1977/78. Side One - 29/ 9/ 1977; Side Two - 16 / 10/ 1978.
Back sleeve lists Stay Free/ Janie Jones/ English Civil War ... but not on
disc. French Bootleg.

Sort it Out (TR 1010)
Side One Safe European Home/ I Fought the Law /
Drug Stabbing Time/ Clash City Rockers /
City of the Dead / English Civil War /
White Man in Hammersmith Palais
Side Two Complete Control/ Cheapskates/
Guns on the Roof / Tommy Gun/
Julie's Working for the Drug Squad / Capital Radio /
London's Burning/ White Riot
Sleeve - Deluxe colour cover

Lyceum, London, 3 January 1979. Japanese Bootleg.

Police (and Firemen) on my Back
(Klashin'Records)
Side One I'm so Bored with the USA/
Drug Stabbing Time/ Jail Guitar Doors/ Tommy Gun/
City of the Dead/ Hate and War/ White Man/
Safe European Home
Side Two Stay Free/ English Civil War/
Guns on the Roof / Police and Thieves /
Capital Radio/ Janie Jones/ Garageland
Sleeve - black & white sleeve

Live at the Agora Theatre, Cleveland 13 Febuary 1979. Cover says 1980
with pictures of NY, but is Cleveland 1979. Red vinyl / 1000 numbered.
American Bootleg.

The Clash Bootleg Bible

Live in Chicago, 14 September 1979.
American Bootleg. Also released as `All or Nothing'

New York, Palladium, 21 September 1979
American Bootleg.

Clash City Rockers
Side One Jimmy Jazz / I'm so Bored with the USA /
Complete Control/ London Calling / Clampdown
Side Two White Man in Hammersmith Palais /
Koka-Kola / I Fought the Law / Jail Guitar Doors/
Police and Thieves
Side Three Stay Free / Clash City Rockers/
Safe European Home/ Capital Radio
Side Four Janie Jones / Garageland /
Armagideon Time/ Career Opportunities/ White Riot
Sleeve - Yellow and black slick cover

Klashing with the Clash (K 100)
Side One Guns of Brixton/ English Civil War /
Clash City Rockers / Stay Free / Clampdown
Side Two Police and Thieves / Capital Radio /
 Tommy Gun
Side Three Safe European Home /
I'm so bored with the USA / Complete Control/
London Calling / White Man in Hammersmith Palais /
Koka-Kola
Side Four Armagideon Time / Career Opportunities /
What's my Name / White Riot
Sleeve - Brown wraparound sleeve

W New FM Broadcast, New York Palladium, 21 September 1979.
Also came in brown sleeve with brown heart on cover.
American Bootleg.

Clampdown USA (Centrifugal 12 Cent-12)
Side One Safe European Home /
I'm so Bored with the USA/ Complete Control/ London
Calling/ White Man in Hammersmith Palais /
Koka-Kola / I Fought the Law
Side Two Jail Guitar Doors/ Guns of Brixton/
English Civil War / Clash City Rockers / Stay Free
Side Three Working for the Clampdown /
 Police and Thieves / Capital Radio / Tommy Gun/
Wrong 'em Boyo
Side Four Janie Jones/ Garageland /
Armagideon Time/ Career Opportunities/
What's my Name/ White Riot
Sleeve - Deluxe, colour front.

**Merry Christmas from CBS Records
(One size fits all AEIOU-121)
Side One** Joy Division - Colony /
The Clash - Tommy Gun / The Jam - David Watts /
XTC - Plans for Nigel/ Elvis Costello - Radio, Radio
Side Two The Cure - Killing an Arab /
Magazine - Give me Everything /
Ultravox - Blue Light / Psychedelic Furs - Mr Jones /
Buzzcocks - You say you don't love me, I believe.
Sleeve - Black & white sticker on white sleeve

Compilation LP Clash track from BBC 2's 'Something Else' TV 11/3/1978.
European bootleg.

**16 Tracks (L2721/1048)
Side One** Clash City Rockers/ Brand New Cadillac /
Safe European Home / Jimmy Jazz / Clampdown /
The Guns of Brixton / Train in Vain / Wrong 'em Boyo
Side Two Koka-Kola /
White Man in Hammersmith Palais / Stay Free/
Rudie can't Fail / Janie Jones / Complete Control /
Armagideon Time/ London Calling
Sleeve - Deluxe red and black cover

Live Hammersmith Odeon supporting Ian Dury & The Blockheads
concert for Kampuchea, 27 December 1979.
Japanese Bootleg.

**Despatches from The Clash Zone (DN)
Side One** Safe European Home / Jimmy Jazz /
Clampdown / The Guns of Brixton / Train in Vain /
Wrong 'em Boyo / Capital Radio / The Prisoner
Side Two London's Burning / White Man / Stay Free/
Rudie can't Fail / Janie Jones / Complete Control /
Armagideon Time/ London Calling
7" Side One - 1-2 Crush on You/ City of the Dead
   Side Two - Pressure Drop
Sleeve - Black & white slick stuck-on cover

live Hammersmith Odeon 27December 79.
7" B-sides. European bootleg.

Capitol Theatre, New Jersey, 8 March 1980.
American Bootleg.

Live in Market Hall Hamburg, 20 May 1980.
European Bootleg.

Hammersmith Palais, 17 June 1980.
Japanese Bootleg.

Capital Crisis (CL 802004)
Side One Sixteen Tons (over P.A.) /
Clash City Rockers / Brand New Cadillac /
Safe European Home / Jimmy Jazz/ London Calling /
The Guns of Brixton
Side Two Train in Vain/
White Man in Hammersmith Palais / Koka-Kola /
I Fought the Law / Spanish Bombs /
Police and Thieves
Side Three Stay Free /
Julie's been working for the Drug Squad /
Wrong 'em Boyo / Working for the Clampdown /
Janie Jones / Complete Control
Side Four Armagideon Time / English Civil War /
Garageland / The Card Cheat / Tommy Gun
Sleeve - Deluxe colour cover

Clash in Hamburg (CL-HH1)
Side One Clash City Rockers / Brand New Cadillac /
Safe European Home / Koka-Kola /
I Fought the Law / White Man in Hammersmith Palais/
48 Hours / Police and Thieves
Side Two Working for the Clampdown /
English Civil War / Janie Jones / London's Burning /
I'm so Bored with the USA / White Riot /
Armagideon Time / Complete Control
Sleeve - Deluxe Black & White sleeve

Clash Songbooks (UD 6543/4)
Side One Clash City Rockers / Brand New Cadillac /
Safe European Home / Jimmy Jazz /
Revolution Rock/ Julie's been working for the Drug
Squad / Guns of Brixton
Side Two Train in Vain / London Calling /
Spanish Bombs / White Man/
Somebody got Murdered/ Koka-Kola /
I Fought the Law / Jail Guitar Doors
Side Three Police and Thieves/ Wrong 'em Boyo/
Clampdown/ Stay Free / English Civil War/
I'm so Bored with the USA/ Complete Control
Side Four Armagideon Time/ Rockers Galore /
Bankrobber/ Tommy Gun/ Capital Radio/
London's Burning/ Janie Jones / What's my Name/
Garageland
Sleeve - Deluxe white and brown sleeve

Impossible Mission, Live in Italy (CI 009)
Side One Intro (Spaghetti Western Music) /
London Calling / Guns of Brixton / Charlie don't Surf /
The Magnificent Seven
Side Two One More Time/ Brand New Cadillac /
Janie Jones / Jimmy Jazz / Armagideon Time/
I Fought the Law / White Riot
Sleeve - Blue spray paint on white background

Live in Bologna, Italy, 20 May 1981. Intro music used `60 seconds to watch' Ennio Morricone's theme for 'A few dollars more' film. Italian Bootleg.

New Speedway (Clash C001)
Side One Intro/ London Calling /
White Man in Hammersmith Palais/ Revolution Rock/
Guns of Brixton / Radio Clash / Complete Control
Side Two Jimmy Jazz/ Armagideon Time/
I Fought the Law / White Riot / Lightning Strikes /
Police and Thieves / Blitzkrieg Bop / London's Burning
Sleeve - Colour gatefold sleeve

Live in Firenze Stadio Communale Florence 23 May 81.
European Bootleg.

Londonderry (MCC 2812-1) (MCC 2812-2)
Side One London Calling / Safe European Home/
White Man/ Train in Vain/ The Call Up
Side Two Ivan meets G.I. Joe / The Leader/
Charlie don't Surf/ The Magnificent Seven/ Bankrobber
Side Three Somebody got Murdered /
Career Opportunities / Working for the Clampdown /
One More Time / Brand New Cadillac / Janie Jones
Side Four Armagideon Time/ I Fought the Law /
London's Burning/ Jimmy Jazz / White Riot
Sleeve - 2 x single LP sleeves; 1/2 Red lettering on
white background; 3/4 Black lettering on
red background

ONDONDERRY ★ THECLA
SH ★ LONDONDERRY ★ TH

Live in Milan, 26 May 1981. European Bootleg.

Up and at 'em (R2B 2630)
Side One Somebody got Murdered/ Radio Clash/
Know your Rights/ Graffiti Rap /
Should I Stay or Should I Go
Side Two The Magnificent Seven /
Ghetto Defendant / Inoculated City /
Hit the Road Jack (Pearl Harbour vocals)
Sleeve - Deluxe black & white with red lettering

Live Theatre Mogador Paris. 30 September 1981. European Bootleg.

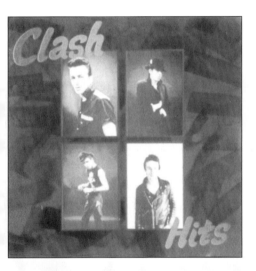

Hits (UD 6572-4)
Side One Know your Rights/ Guns of Brixton / Train in Vain/
White Man **Side Two** The Magnificent Seven /
Clash City Rockers/ Koka-Kola / Ivan meets G.I. Joe/
Junco Partner **Side Three** The Leader/ I Fought the Law/
Ghetto Defendant / Graffiti Rap/
Side Four Somebody got Murdered / London Calling /
Clampdown / Radio Clash **Side Five** The Call Up /
Bankrobber / Complete Control / Lightning Strikes /
Charlie don't Surf / Spanish Bombs **Side Six** Broadway /
I don't Like/ One More Time / Brand New Cadillac /
Janie Jones / Armagideon Time/ London's Burning /
White Riot
Sleeve - Deluxe colour cover

Sides 1, 2, 3 & 4 - Live at Lyceum Ballroom, London, 19 October 1981
Sides 5 & 6 - Live at Bonds Club, New York, June 1981. Japanese Bootleg

Combat Rock Outtakes (Love Situation)
Side One Straight to Hell/ Know your Rights /
Rock the Casbah / Ghetto Defendant
Side Two Sean Flynn/ Car Jamming/ Atom Tan/
The Beautiful People/ First Night Back in London /
Inoculated City
Sleeve - Deluxe colour sleeve, green border

1982 Outtakes for Combat Rock LP. An important release, as it contains some of
Mick Jones' original mixes of Combat Rock tracks plus the still un-released
`The Beautiful People'. Italian Bootleg.

White Riot (Nordsee Records 50 083)
Side One London Calling/ Safe European Home/
White Man in Hammersmith Palais /
Brand New Cadillac / Charlie don't Surf / Clampdown
Side Two This is Radio Clash / Armagideon Time/
Jimmy Jazz / Tommy Gun / Fujiyama Mama /
Police on my Back / White Riot
Sleeve - Green and black sleeve

Live at Sun Plaza Hall, Tokyo, 1 February 1982.
Japanese TV broadcast.
Track listing wrong on sleeve. European Bootleg.

Death or Glory (CR015)
Side One Train in Vain / Washington Bullets /
Ivan meets G.I. Joe / Career Opportunities /
Janie Jones / Clash City Rockers / London's Burning
Side Two Junco Partner / Spanish Bombs /
Bankrobber / Radio Clash / I Fought the Law /
London Calling / Tommy Gun
Sleeve - Deluxe red and green cover

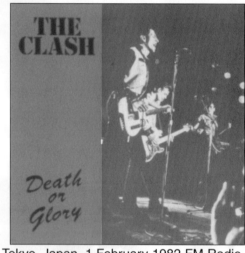

Side One - Live at Sun Plaza, Tokyo, Japan, 1 February 1982 FM Radio
Side Two - Tracks 1-4 Jamaica Music Festival, 27 November 1982
Side Two - Tracks 5-6 Strummer with Pogues, Irish TV, 1988
Side Two - Track 7 Something Else TV Show, 1978.

L*I*V*E
Side One London Calling / Safe European Home /
Guns of Brixton / Train in Vain / Know your Rights /
Magnificent Seven
Side Two Ghetto Defendant /
Should I Stay or Should I Go / Police and Thieves /
Brand New Cadillac / Bankrobber /
Complete Control
Sleeve - Black & white stuck on slick cover

Live at Lochem Festival, 20 May 1982. Also came later
with colour sleeve. European Bootleg.

**Down at the Casbah Club
(Butch Prod BP205568)**
Side One Guns of Brixton/ Somebody got Murdered/ White Man / Career Opportunities
Side Two Magnificent Seven / Train in Vain / One More Time / Radio Clash / Rock the Casbah
Side Three Police on my Back / Brand New Cadillac / Clampdown / Bankrobber / Armagideon Time
Side Four Should I Stay or Should I Go / I Fought the Law / Straight to Hell / Stay Free / Garageland
Sleeve - Deluxe silver, red and black sleeve

Live Brixton 'Fair Deal' London, 17 July 1982. American Bootleg.

Stinkfoot in Hollywood (Cash Disque)
Side One Combat Rock / Train in Vain / Bankrobber / Junkie Slip / Rock the Casbah / Radio Clash
Side Two Should I Stay or Should I Go / Brand New Cadillac / Police and Thieves / Armagideon Time/ Somebody got Murdered / I Fought the Law / Straight to Hell
Sleeve - Black & White cover

Live at Hollywood Palladium, 18 June 1982. European Bootleg.

Come Back (Logo Record)
Side One Are you Red...y / Rock & Roll City / The Dictator / This is England / Daddy in the Street / We are The Clash
Side Two Safe European Home / Clampdown / I'm so Bored with the USA / Should I Stay or Should I Go / Garageland/ Spanish Bombs / White Riot
Sleeve - Colour picture disc. Side One yellow background; Side Two red background

Live in Palasport Milan, Italy 27 February 1984. European Bootleg.

The Clash Bootleg Bible

Five Alive (SCRAP Records 198-40217)
Side One London Calling / Safe European Home/
Know your Rights/ Band Intro/ Are you Red...y /
Rock the Casbah / Sex Mad Roar
Side Two Clampdown / Guns of Brixton /
The Dictator / Complete Control /
White Man in Hammersmith Palais / This is England
Side Three Police and Thieves / Three Card Trick /
Garageland / This is Radio Clash / Janie Jones /
I Fought the Law
Side Four Glue Zombie / Tommy Gun /
We are The Clash / Brand New Cadillac /
Armagideon Time / I'm so Bored with the USA /
English Civil War / White Riot
Sleeve - Deluxe green and white cover

Live Isstadion,Stockholm Sweden 17 February 1984.
European Bootleg.

Dusseldorf '84 (Guilty M-11/A)
Side One London Calling / Safe European Home /
Are you Red...y / Rock the Casbah / Guns of Brixton /
Bored with the USA
Side Two Should I Stay or Should I Go /
Police and Thieves / Armagideon Time/
I Fought the Law / Brand New Cadillac /
English Civil War / White Riot
Sleeve - White cover, green stamped.

Live Philipshalle Dusseldorf, 19 February 1984, Clear vinyl.
German Bootleg.

We don't miss Mick Jones (PR-84-331)
Side One Tommy Gun/ Janie Jones /
Are you Red...y / Rock the Casbah / The Dictator/
Clash City Rockers / I'm so Bored with the USA
Side Two I Fought the Law / We are The Clash /
Complete Control / Garageland / Armagideon Time /
Radio Clash / White Riot
Sleeve - Black & White cover

Live at Festhalle Bern, Switzerland, 25 February 1984.
Green vinyl. European Bootleg.

The Clash Bootleg Bible

Live Espace Ballard Paris 1st March 1984,
French Bootleg.

Live in Paris (LP 9)
Side One Safe European Home /
Are you Red...y / Rock the Casbah /
The Dictator / Guns of Brixton / Sex Mad Roar/
I'm so Bored with the USA
Side Two This is England / Tommy Gun /
Three Card Trick / Janie Jones / Armagideon Time /
White Man in Hammersmith Palais
Sleeve - Deluxe black and grey cover

Live at Brixton Academy, London, 6 December 1984.
European Bootleg.

One More Time (CL 61284)
Side One One More Time/ London's Burning /
Complete Control / Radio Clash / Spanish Bombs
Side Two Rock the Casbah / North and South /
Are you Red...y / Fingerpoppin' / What's my Name /
The Dictator / Capital Radio
Sleeve - Black & white cover

Recorded live at Gateshead Station, 11 May 1985, the band busking
acoustically outside the station. European Bootleg.

Back to Basics
Side One Movers and Shakers / Cool under Heat /
Guns of Brixton / Spanish Bombs /
Police on my Back / Jimmy Jazz /
White Man in Hammersmith Palais
Side Two Straight to Hell / Clash City Rockers /
I Fought the Law / Brand New Cadillac /
White Riot / Bankrobber / Stepping Stone
Sleeve - Black lettering on green and white
background

The Clash UK Gig Guide ...
Confirmed Sightings

1976

4 /7 /76	Black Swan, Sheffield	**Five Man**
13 /8 /76	Rehearsals Rehearsals Camden Town, London (Private invite only)	**Clash Line Up (1)**
29 /8 /76	Screen on the Green, Islington, London	
31 /8 /76	100 Club, Oxford Street, London	
5 /9 /76	The Roundhouse, Camden Town, London	

20 /9 /76	100 Club, Oxford Street, London............	**100 Club Punk Festival**

9 /10 /76	Tiddenfoot Leisure Centre, Leyton Buzzard	
15 /10 /76	Acklam Hall, Ladbroke Grove, London	
16 /10 /76	University of London	
23 /10 /76	Institute of Contemporary Arts, London	
27 /10 /76	Barbarellas, Birmingham	
29 /10 /76	Town Hall, Fulham, London	

5 /11 /76	Royal College of Art, London..............	**A Night Of Treason**

11 /11 /76	Lacy Lady, Ilford	
18 /11 /76	Nag's Head, High Wycombe	
29 /11 /76	Lancaster Polytechnic, Coventry	

6 /12 /76	Polytechnic, Leeds......................	**Anarchy Tour**
9 /12 /76	Electric Circus, Manchester................	
14 /12 /76	Castle Cinema, Caerphilly, Wales............	**Dates Played**
19 /12 /76	Electric Circus, Manchester................	
20 /12 /76	Winter Gardens, Cleethorpes...............	
21 /12 /76	Woods Centre, Plymouth..................	**With**
22 /12 /76	Woods Centre, Plymouth..................	**Sex Pistols**

The Clash UK Gig Guide ...
Confirmed Sightings

1977

1/1/77	Roxy Club, Covent Garden, London
11/3/77	Coliseum, Harlesden, London
1/5/77	Civic Hall, Guildford
2/5/77	Rascals, Chester
3/5/77	Barbarellas, Birmingham
4/5/77	Affair, Swindon
5/5/77	Erics, Liverpool
6/5/77	University, Aberdeen
7/5/77	Playhouse, Edinburgh
8/5/77	Electric Circus, Manchester
9/5/77	Rainbow, London
10/5/77	Town Hall, Kidderminster
12/5/77	Palais, Nottingham
13/5/77	Polytechnic, Leicester
15/5/77	Fiesta, Plymouth
16/5/77	University, Swansea
17/5/77	Polytechnic, Leeds
19/5/77	Rock Garden, Middlesborough
20/5/77	University, Newcastle
21/5/77	City Hall, St Albans
22/5/77	Skindles, Maidenhead
23/5/77	Top of the World, Stafford
24/5/77	Top Rank, Cardiff
25/5/77	Polytechnic, Brighton
26/5/77	Colston, Bristol
27/5/77	Pavilion, West Runton
28/5/77	Odeon, Canterbury
29/5/77	Chancellor, Chelmsford
30/5/77	California, Dunstable

'White Riot' Tour

The Clash UK Gig Guide ...
Confirmed Sightings

1977

20/10/77	Ulster Hall, Belfast
21/10/77	Trinity College, Dublin
24/10/77	Kinema, Dumfermline
25/10/77	Apollo, Glasgow
26/10/77	Clouds, Edinburgh
27/10/77	University, Leeds
28/10/77	Polytechnic, Newcastle
29/10/77	Apollo, Manchester
30/10/77	Victoria, Stoke
1/11/77	Top Rank, Sheffield
2/11/77	University, Bradford
3/11/77	Kings Hall, Derby
4/11/77	University, Cardiff
6/11/77	Market Hall, Carlisle
7/11/77	Top Rank, Birmingham
8/11/77	Locarno, Coventry
9/11/77	Winter Gardens, Bournemouth
10/11/77	Exhibition Centre, Bristol
11/11/77	Corn Exchange, Cambridge
12/11/77	Pavilion, Hastings
13/11/77	Top Rank, Southampton
13/12/77	Rainbow, London
14/12/77	Rainbow, London
15/12/77	Rainbow, London

'Out Of Control' Tour

1978

30/4/78	Victoria Park, Hackney...............

Rock Against Racism Gig

28/6/78	Friars, Aylesbury
29/6/78	Queens Hall, Leeds
30/6/78	Top Rank, Sheffield
1/7/78	Granby Hall, Leicester
2/7/78	Apollo, Manchester
4/7/78	Apollo, Glasgow
5/7/78	Music Hall, Aberdeen
6/7/78	Leisure Centre, Chester
8/7/78	Sports Centre, Crawley
9/7/78	Locarno, Bristol
10/7/78	Town Hall, Torquay

'Out On Parole' Tour

The Clash UK Gig Guide ... Confirmed Sightings

1978

11/7/78	Top Rank, Cardiff	
12/7/78	Top Rank, Birmingham	**'Out On Parole' Tour**
24/7/78	Music Machine, London	
25/7/78	Music Machine, London	
26/7/78	Music Machine, London	
27/7/78	Music Machine, London	
25/10/78	Roxy Theatre, Harlesden, London	
26/10/78	Roxy Theatre, Harlesden, London	
16/11/78	Odeon, Edinburgh	
17/11/78	Town Hall, Middlesborough	
18/11/78	University, Leeds	**'Sort it Out' Tour**
19/11/78	Top Rank, Sheffield	
20/11/78	De Montford, Leicester	
21/11/78	Locarno, Bristol	
22/11/78	Village Bowl, Bournemouth	
23/11/78	Apollo, Manchester	
24/11/78	Kings Hall, Derby	
26/11/78	Top Rank, Cardiff	
27/11/78	University, Exeter	
28/11/78	Tiffanys, Coventry	
29/11/78	Victoria Hall, Stoke	
30/11/78	Wirrana, Peterborough	
2/12/78	Polytechnic, Newcastle	
4/12/78	University, Glasgow	
5/12/78	University, Glasgow	
6/12/78	University, Liverpool	
18/12/78	Tiffanys, Purley	
19/12/78	Music Machine, London	**Sid Vicious Defence Fund Benefit**
22/12/78	Friars, Aylesbury	
28/12/78	Lyceum, London	**'Sort it Out' Tour**
29/12/78	Lyceum, London	

1979

3/1/79	Lyceum, London	

The Clash UK Gig Guide ...
Confirmed Sightings

1979

5/7/79	Notre Dame Hall, London	**Secret Gigs**
6/7/79	Notre Dame Hall, London	
14/7/79	Rainbow, London	**Southall Defence Fund**
25/12/79	Acklam Hall, Ladbroke Grove, London	**Secret Gigs**
26/12/79	Acklam Hall, Ladbroke Grove, London	
27/12/79	Hammersmith Odeon, London	**Concert for Kampuchea**

1980

5/1/80	Friars, Aylesbury
6/1/80	Odeon, Canterbury
8/1/80	Top Rank, Brighton
9/1/80	Top Rank, Brighton
11/1/80	Leisure Centre, Crawley
12/1/80	Pavilion, Hastings
13/1/80	Locarno, Bristol
14/1/80	Gaumont, Ipswich
16/1/80	De Montford, Leicester
18/1/80	Caird Hall, Dundee
19/1/80	Odeon, Edinburgh
20/1/80	Odeon, Edinburgh
21/1/80	Apollo, Glasgow
22/1/80	Apollo, Glasgow
23/1/80	University, Lancaster
24/1/80	Tiffanys, Blackpool
25/1/80	King Georges, Blackburn
26/1/80	Leisure Centre, Chester
27/1/80	Top Rank, Sheffield
29/1/80	St Georges, Bradford
30/1/80	Royal Hall, Bridlington
31/1/80	University, Leeds
1/2/80	Victoria Hall, Hanley
3/2/80	Apollo, Manchester
4/2/80	Apollo, Manchester
5/2/80	Top Rank, Birmingham
6/2/80	Top Rank, Birmingham
7/2/80	Tiffanys, Coventry
9/2/80	Guildhall, Portsmouth

'The Sixteen Tons' Tour

The Clash UK Gig Guide ...
Confirmed Sightings

1980

10/2/80	Wessex Hall, Poole
11/2/80	Sophia Gardens, Cardiff
12/2/80	Stateside, Bournemouth
13/2/80	Top Rank, Southampton
15/2/80	Electric Ballroom, London
16/2/80	Electric Ballroom, London
17/2/80	Lyceum, London
18/2/80	Odeon, Lewisham
16/6/80	Hammersmith Palais, London
17/6/80	Hammersmith Palais, London

'The Sixteen Tons' Tour

1981

5/10/81	Apollo, Manchester
6/10/81	Apollo, Manchester
7/10/81	Apollo, Glasgow
8/10/81	Apollo, Glasgow
10/10/81	Lyceum, Sheffield
12/10/81	Royal Court, Liverpool
15/10/81	Coliseum, St Austell
18/10/81	Lyceum, London
19/10/81	Lyceum, London
20/10/81	Lyceum, London
21/10/81	Lyceum, London
22/10/81	Lyceum, London
25/10/81	Lyceum, London
26/10/81	Lyceum, London

'Radio Clash' Tour

The Clash UK Gig Guide ...
Confirmed Sightings
1982

10/7/82	Fair Deal, Brixton
11/7/82	Fair Deal, Brixton
12/7/82	Sport Centre, Stoke
13/7/82	Victoria Hall, Hanley
14/7/82	City Hall, Newcastle
15/7/82	City Hall, Newcastle
17/7/82	Fair Deal, Brixton
18/7/82	Bingley Hall, Birmingham
19/7/82	Assembly Rooms, Derby
20/7/82	De Montford, Leicester
22/7/82	Leisure Centre, Irvine
23/7/82	Playhouse, Edinburgh
24/7/82	Ice Rink, Inverness
26/7/82	University, Leeds
27/7/82	Arts Centre, Poole
28/7/82	Guildhall, Portsmouth
30/7/82	Fair Deal, Brixton
31/7/82	Fair Deal, Brixton
2/8/82	Locarno, Bristol
3/8/82	Locarno, Bristol

'Down at the Casbah Club' Tour

The Clash UK Gig Guide ... Confirmed Sightings

1984

5/2/84	SFX, Dublin
6/2/84	SFX, Dublin
7/2/84	Ulster Hall, Belfast
8/2/84	Ulster Hall, Belfast
10/2/84	Barrowlands, Glasgow
11/2/84	Apollo, Manchester
12/2/84	De Montford, Leicester
13/2/84	Colston, Bristol
3/3/84	Playhouse, Edinburgh
4/3/84	King Georges, Blackburn
5/3/84	Royal Court, Liverpool
6/3/84	Guildhall, Portsmouth
8/3/84	Academy, Brixton
9/3/84	Academy, Brixton
10/3/84	Academy, Brixton
12/3/84	Ulster Hall, Belfast
13/3/84	SFX, Dublin
14/3/84	SFX, Dublin
16/3/84	Academy, Brixton
17/3/84	Academy, Brixton
6/12/84	Academy, Brixton
7/12/84	Academy, Brixton

'Out Of Control' Tour
Five Man Clash Line Up (2)

Scargil's Xmas Party Miner's Benefit Gig

First gig black swan Sheffield 4 Sept 1976

Last gig Athens Greece 27 Aug 1985

Nine years inbetween

Drummers, Managers.....Came and Went.

'Garage Band' ..to 'Stadium Band'

Reunion..Never say Never.....

STAY FREE.....

VIVA. THE CLASH.

VIVA. ROCK 'N' ROLL.....